Counseling
and
AIDS

RESOURCES FOR
CHRISTIAN COUNSELING

RESOURCES FOR CHRISTIAN COUNSELING

VOLUME TWENTY-FOUR

Counseling
and
AIDS

GREGG R. ALBERS, M.D.

RESOURCES FOR
CHRISTIAN COUNSELING

—————— General Editor ——————

Gary R. Collins, Ph.D.

WORD PUBLISHING
Dallas · London · Vancouver · Melbourne

Library of Congress Cataloging-in-Publication Data

Albers, Gregg R., 1955–
    Counseling and AIDS / Gregg R. Albers.
        p.   cm. — (Resources for Christian counseling ; v. 24)
    Includes bibliographical references and index.
    ISBN 0–8499–0695–4
    1. AIDS (Disease)—Patients—Counseling of.   2. Pastoral
counseling. I. Title. II. Series.
RC607.A26A3687   1990
362.1′969792—dc20

4 9 AGF 9 8 7 6 5 4 3

Printed in the United States of America

CONTENTS

EDITOR'S PREFACE

"AIDS is one of the most serious health problems that has ever faced the American public."

With these words, the U.S. Surgeon General began an eight-page brochure that was prepared by his office and the Centers for Disease Control and sent to every home in the United States. When the copy came to our house, I skimmed it and filed it away for future reference.

I wonder how many others did the same. I also wonder how many people tossed the report away with the junk mail and gave the issue no more thought.

It is easy for any of us to assume that AIDS is a problem for other people. We have seen the warnings in the media. We have read that more than a million Americans carry the AIDS virus. We realize that millions of others—spouses, lovers, children, parents, friends—will be profoundly affected by the disease. We have read about famous people and promising young professionals whose lives have ended prematurely because of

AIDS-related illnesses. We have heard and perhaps been annoyed by the judgmental, condemning, and holier-than-thou attitudes of some prominent preachers who lack compassion for and sensitivity to AIDS sufferers. Most of us know that the AIDS epidemic goes far beyond drug users or the homosexual community. We have encountered the debates about "safe sex" and the use of condoms. We have heard repeatedly that AIDS is not spread by handshakes, toilet seats, or contaminated doorknobs. And most of us have heard how entire nations, especially in Africa, are in danger of being wiped out within the next few years if the influence and spread of this deadly disease is not stopped.

But all of this seems far removed from our everyday lives—until we meet a person with AIDS, discover that a child with AIDS has been banned from a local Sunday school, or learn that somebody we know has tested positive for HIV, the AIDS virus. It is then that the reality hits home and we begin to recognize the true pathos and pain of the plague in our midst.

For Gregg Albers, AIDS is no faraway issue. The moving and dramatic case histories that appear in the following pages show how the author has met and treated a number of AIDS patients. As a Christian physician, he has stood by the bedsides of people who were dying with AIDS and has comforted their loved ones. He has talked at length with AIDS victims who have been abandoned by their families, friends, and churches. He has been present when unsuspecting people, including Christians, have been shocked to learn that they tested positive for HIV—not because of their own promiscuity or drug abuse, but because of a spouse who was thought to be faithful, but whose secret promiscuous behavior carried AIDS into the marriage.

Dr. Albers goes beyond the stories to provide practical guidance to anyone who counsels with AIDS victims or their friends and relatives. The author gives an up-to-date, well-documented, professionally sound, and biblically astute consideration of the AIDS issue. He has produced a much-needed book for the Christian community.

Like the other volumes in the Resources for Christian Counseling series, this book is intended to be practical and helpful. Written by counseling experts, each of whom has a strong

Christian commitment and extensive counseling experience, the books are meant to be examples of accurate psychology and careful use of Scripture. Each volume is intended to have a clear evangelical perspective, careful documentation, a strong practical orientation, and freedom from the sweeping statements and undocumented rhetoric that sometimes characterize writing in the counseling field. Our goal is to provide books that are clearly written, useful, up-to-date overviews of the issues faced by contemporary Christian counselors—including pastoral counselors. All of the Resources for Christian Counseling books have similar bindings and together they are intended to comprise a helpful encyclopedia of Christian counseling.

This is the second book that Dr. Gregg Albers has written for the series. While he was writing *Counseling the Sick and Terminally Ill*, I was searching for somebody who could write a book on AIDS. I knew that Gregg had an interest in this topic and I knew that he had written a book entitled *Plague in Our Midst: Sexuality, AIDS and the Christian Family.* But I did not know at the time how much he had worked with AIDS patients and neither did I realize the extent of his expertise in this area. While working with Dr. Albers on the other book, I almost missed the opportunity to have him write this crucially important volume on AIDS.

As you read the following pages, I suspect you will agree that this is an excellent and helpful treatment of a significant topic. Scientifically accurate, the book is frequently moving and consistently shows the author's deep commitment to Christ. Dr. Albers is a physician who cares about people and knows about AIDS.

You may have misplaced or tossed aside the Surgeon General's report on AIDS. But this book is a publication that you are likely to keep and consult repeatedly, especially if the AIDS epidemic continues to gallop as rapidly as the experts predict.

Gary R. Collins, Ph.D.
Kildeer, Illinois

PART ONE

UNDERSTANDING AIDS
VICTIMS AND THE DISEASE

CHAPTER ONE

AIDS: THE VICTIMS

Tina

Lying alone in a cool, damp basement apartment, Tina began to cry. Waves of self-pity rolled over her frail body like a strong pair of hands wringing water out of a wet towel. She knew that her decision to give up her baby for adoption to an established family was best for her and her newborn baby boy. But she was not comforted. She lay tossing in a restless cold sweat.

Her fears for her new son were as real as the remembered pain of her labor contractions and the joy she had experienced when she heard the proclamation, "It's a healthy boy." His cries had been vibrant and healthy; but she knew that, as he grew, he had between a 25 and 50 percent chance of developing AIDS.

She knew this because she had known for the last four months—since late in her pregnancy—that she was HIV positive, that she had been exposed to and had contracted AIDS.

She wanted so much to be there if her son got sick, to comfort and nurse him. But the thought of her baby dying of AIDS was almost more than she could bear. Again, she collapsed into a sobbing, limp mass on her bed.

Tina's short-lived affair with Roger had fallen apart after only three episodes of intercourse, twice while using a condom. Then weeks had passed before she developed a painful vaginal rash. It had only lasted a few days, though, so she wasn't that concerned. A few months into the pregnancy the same rash recurred—but more severely. She went to an STD (sexually transmitted disease) clinic because she feared that Roger had given her herpes.

Her pregnancy was now well progressed and the physician in the STD clinic warned her about having her child vaginally if she did have herpes. He suggested that he confirm his diagnosis with a smear from the vaginal secretions as well as taking a blood test. Then she was started on medication for the herpes infection because it was such a severe case.

When she returned two weeks later, the rash was doing much better. But the doctor very dryly stated, "You don't need to worry much about the herpes. That is not nearly as important as the other infection your boyfriend gave you—AIDS."

"How could I be dying of a deadly disease?" Tina asked the physician. "I only had sex with him three times! Condoms are supposed to protect you from this! How could God be so cruel? I'm not gay and I'm not a drug abuser. How could I get this disease? Why can't they just treat this infection with an antibiotic and make it go away? What about my baby? Am I going to watch my baby die? Why is this payment for my sin so severe?"

After the physician tried to calm her hysterical crying, Tina retreated to her tiny basement apartment. All through the pregnancy, she was able to hide both the herpes and AIDS infections from her second obstetrician. She knew that if he found out about the herpes, other questions and tests would soon follow. Once she had made her decision to give up the child for adoption, she sought a lawyer who could arrange the transfer with as few questions as possible. Her decision was so private even her family and closest friends were unaware of the real reason she was giving away her precious child. Day by day her love for this unborn child grew.

After the birth, Tina kept track of her child through reports she received from the lawyer as part of the adoption agreement. A little more than two years after the birth, she was overcome with a severe case of pneumonia, and was hospitalized, where she was comforted by the last report she would receive: The baby was still healthy.

Tina died after spending two weeks in the hospital. Her son died later that same year of a severe herpes infection of the brain. The adoptive parents found out their beautiful child was stricken with HIV the last week of his short but well-loved life.

Gary

"It can't be bleeding so soon," Gary stated with disgust.

He was accustomed to bleeding into the joints, a normal occurrence for most hemophiliacs. But this episode just would not stop after repeated injections of Factor VIII. The usual remedies of ice packs and two days of rest were not doing the trick this time.

"Your doctor said we should go to the hospital and get some blood tests. He ordered them to be done as soon as we get there," his mother said.

Within the hour, Gary was admitted for emergency treatment of his blood problem. Tests revealed that not only was his blood deficient in Factor VIII, a clotting factor needed to stop bleeding, but his platelets, another important part of the clotting process, also had fallen to dangerously low levels. He was at risk of dying from internal bleeding at any time.

Gary's bouts of depression and fits of rage were characteristic of the frustration he felt about his blood disease. It was difficult to be a handicapped young man who was unable to participate in contact sports when many of his friends enjoyed football and basketball, sports that were the social bread and butter of high-school males. Yet he never showed this side of his personality to his friends or at the church where his father was deacon. Many people marveled at the God-given grace Gary portrayed when dealing with his disease in public. Most of the people who regularly prayed for him just asked, "Why?"

Perseverance through the trials and testings of his disease had molded Gary into a young champion, and academically, he was at the top of his class. His involvement in a number of community projects brought attention to the plight of persons with hemophilia. Consistency and hard work were the characteristics his church family attributed to this not so typical "sick kid." He even excelled in his hobby of model building, a joy he shared often with his father.

Once he arrived at the hospital, the routine blood work was begun, including an HIV titer (AIDS test), which was added because of the many transfusions Gary had needed. After three days of treatments, the earthshaking news was given to Gary and his parents: He was positive. Somewhere along the line, he had been given HIV-infected Factor VIII. The remainder of the hospitalization became a blur.

After the initial shock had worn off, Gary and his parents sat down to discuss what could be done. They all felt comfortable trying a high-dose vitamin and mineral regimen along with a home-schooling plan to complete his high-school course work. They did not want to risk the possibility of rejection and media attention if other students or parents discovered the secret. He and his family did everything in their power to prevent bringing even simple infections into their home. They also switched to heat-treated Factor VIII to prevent Gary from continued exposure to the AIDS virus.

Their efforts were rewarded with an extra year of life. Gary was able to finish his junior year at home before he became ill with Pneumocystis carinii pneumonia and was moved to a teaching hospital in the area. There, even the best medical care was unable to prolong his life more than a week. He died peacefully with full assurance that his new home was prepared for him in heaven.

Gary's death was extremely difficult for his mother. She had lost another son, also a hemophiliac, when he had bled to death. Because she was the carrier of the gene that had killed her precious children, the guilt she bore and the loss of both sons to complications of this dreaded blood disease were more than she could stand. Before the funeral arrangements had been made, Gary's father had to commit her to a local psychiatric hospital. Although she showed significant improvement after the second month of hospitalization, she relapsed quickly when she came home and was reminded of her role in the boys' deaths.

It was almost a year before Gary's father could mention in public what had caused his son's death. He could not understand how Gary's innocence could be defiled by "AIDS—the disease of perversion." Now he has developed a great one-on-one ministry to AIDS victims, and to families who have lost a loved one to AIDS.

Carolyn

"Is this Mrs. Hopewell?" the man on the phone asked.

"Yes, this is she," said Carolyn.

"This is Dr. Martin, your husband's physician. Your husband asked me today in the hospital to call you—because he wasn't sure how to tell you what needs to be said. He also wanted me to answer any questions that you might have."

"You mean his illness is quite serious?" she asked with a hushed voice.

"Mrs. Hopewell, your husband is dying of pneumonia because he is infected with AIDS. He is not responding to the strongest antibiotics that we have," Dr. Martin stated.

"How could he get AIDS?" Carolyn asked with surprise.

"Your husband has told us how he contracted the illness. Why don't you ask your best friend to babysit for a few hours so that you can talk with him at length about his life before you were married. You need to talk this out with him. And please do it within the next few days, because his condition is deteriorating quite rapidly," the doctor said.

The night before their talk, Carolyn's mind raced with thoughts of some heinous act Danny might have performed—rape, murder, robbery, some unfaithful act with a prostitute. She was unable to sleep; and there was so much fear in her heart, she was totally unable to pray.

She left Tasha, their eighteen-month-old child, with a close friend and took the bus downtown to General City Hospital the next morning.

"Carolyn, you've got to believe me when I say that I love you with my whole heart—because I do!" Danny stated as forcefully as his ailing lungs could muster.

"When I was small, my stepfather sexually used me. He and his friends had sex with me more times than I could count. In college, I seemed to attract a number of homosexual friends, and we had sex every weekend or so. Yet homosexuality never seemed enough. I had some heterosexual intercourse, but I never really loved anyone until you came into my life. You cared for me in ways that no one has ever cared for me before. I love you Carolyn," Danny said with tears pouring down his cheeks.

"How on earth can you say you love me, when you hid all these relationships from me for the last three years?" she asked in anger.

"I didn't want to hurt you!" he said as he sobbed uncontrollably.

"Couldn't you stop?" Carolyn asked in a calmer voice.

"You'll never know how strong this addiction is. Every time I tried to stop, my lover would call me at work and entice me to come over at lunch. Just the pictures he has hanging in his apartment were enough to get me going," he said, punctuating his explanation with coughing episodes.

"Couldn't you have asked for help?" Carolyn whispered as she continued to cry.

"I loved you too much to admit that I was bisexual. Even after we accepted Christ at that Bible study, my urges seemed to control me. I prayed for deliverance and seemed to do better for a while. But then Joey would call again, remind me of my stinking past, and my affairs with him and Al. Then he threatened me. He said if I even thought of going straight he would call you. I didn't want you to be hurt by that . . . I am sorry that you had to find out this way," Danny said quietly.

Carolyn couldn't speak through her sobs.

"I believe that this AIDS thing is God's way of delivering me from this life style that I hate and yet can't get away from," Danny continued.

"I forgive you . . . and I will love you forever," Carolyn said as she bent over the bed to kiss him. They held each other for almost an hour without saying a word. Then Carolyn had to leave to pick up Tasha.

They were able to see each other three more times before Danny lapsed into a coma and died quietly in his sleep.

Since her husband's death, Carolyn has reconstructed her life. The local technical college gave her a scholarship so she could finish her secretarial training. But her greatest ministry is in the inner-city churches where she speaks about sexual problems and AIDS, sharing her sorrows and burdens.

Carolyn's last test for HIV was negative.

Cese

The weather was beautiful. No one could have asked for a more typical Southern California day. However, none of the young adults at Hoover High School lingered in the sun for long, because the school assembly was about to begin.

The auditorium was packed. The special speaker that day was a seventeen-year-old girl, a wispy blonde with large blue eyes. Her figure seemed thin for her medium frame. The students quickly hushed as she walked to the podium.

"My name is Cecelia, Cese for short. I want to tell you my story."

All the publicity surrounding this assembly had been aimed at venereal disease and AIDS. The students wondered how such a pretty, young girl could be speaking to them about these difficult topics.

"I attend a high school upstate. My parents, my teachers, my counselors have all asked me to share my story with you. It's a sad story, so please excuse me if I cry when I tell it, and I'll excuse you if you cry," Cese said with a small grin.

"Like most freshman, I was overwhelmed when a senior asked me out on a date. He seemed so mature. We went to one of the nicest restaurants in our town. After that we went to a movie and then to watch the moon over the ocean. It was so romantic. I am not sure that I have ever had such a good time with a guy.

"But then we started to kiss, and he started to touch me where I didn't want to be touched. Even though he said he loved me, he seemed almost like an uncontrollable animal . . . then he raped me. He said it felt so good. But I felt so terrible, so dirty afterward. All I could do was cry. He drove me home and said he would call me the next day. He never did. I never heard from him again.

"I couldn't tell my parents what had happened. I really sweated for the next three weeks until my period started. Then everything seemed to go all right, even though I had a few nightmares about the episode on the beach.

"Two years later I was admitted to the hospital for pneumonia. My doctor came in with my parents and said they had to talk with me. They started to ask me questions about intravenous drugs and having sex, but I still couldn't tell them about my being raped. Then they told me that I had AIDS and that I needed to be honest with them.

"Do you know what it is like to be told you have AIDS? The anger, the denial, and the confusion all seemed to be present at the same time. The next day I described my only sexual encounter—first to my doctor, and later to my parents. We cried at first. After I was discharged from the hospital, we prayed and talked with our pastor about how we could help others to avoid this terrible disease.

"That's why I am here today. You all need to know this: AIDS can infect teens like you and like me. And you need to know that having sex or using drugs is just not worth the risk. Forgive me if I use the 'C' word, but condom or not, clean needles or not, it's just not worth the risk."

Cese's program was a huge success. I have been told that all of the other health-education programs combined were not as effective as Cese's story at changing the attitudes of students toward sexual promiscuity. Other teen-age AIDS victims have joined Cese in speaking to their peers about their path to contracting the disease.

Cese is still sharing her story with teens to this day. She is also sharing God's love through her private witness after these assemblies.

Jay

The group from a Chicago inner-city church had just arrived in Haiti to help build school and support buildings for a ministry there. Jay was one of the college students who was leading the group of about twenty high-school students who had committed four weeks of their summer and raised the support needed to be part of this outreach to the desolate and poor of Haiti. Their excitement grew into joy as they entered into the ministry compound.

Even though most of the students had their bottles of stomach remedies with them, Jay and three other students became violently ill with diarrhea and stomach cramps. No other alternatives appeared open as they cautiously entered the small clinic in the local town. They had been warned by the minister's wife to take only injections if they were offered any medication, because the oral medications were often expired or contaminated.

The clinic could not have been more devastating to the senses, even after the warnings they had received. The waiting room reeked of sweat, urine, and vomit. There was no light except that given by the doorless entrance. Moans and cries seemed to drown out the nurse's call for patients. When their turn finally came, the nurse asked them a few questions in broken English. As they had been instructed, they pointed at their arms. She pulled out her syringe, loaded it with medication, then gave each of them an injection.

Though the weakness seemed to last for a few days, the diarrhea and stomach cramps stopped later that day. They thanked God for their relief and went to work mixing mortar and carrying bricks.

Almost nine years later, Jay lay in his hospital bed thinking of that summer. He remembered how he had thanked God for the injection that had stopped the discomfort. Now he couldn't understand how God, who was supposed to be in control of his life, would let him destroy it through a simple injection. His newly diagnosed case of AIDS could only have come through that Haitian needle, because Jay was still a virgin; he had never had a blood transfusion or injected illegal drugs. As he began to pray, he paused for a few seconds, then prayed out loud, "God, how can I thank you for AIDS?"

Jay's trials and tests were many. He was asked to give up his position as the youth minister at a local Baptist church as soon as the deacons board heard he had the disease. A number of families from the church shunned him and refused to help him during his prolonged recovery from pneumonia. Only a few of the widows came to see him, bringing him the fruits of their kitchen labors, always in disposable containers. Many of the kids in the youth group sent cards or called on the phone, but most were not allowed by their parents to see him.

His mother had died from a heart attack six months before his diagnosis with AIDS. His father had never cared about him after he and Jay's mother were divorced when Jay was twelve. Jay had a sister who called him, sent him cards for his birthday, and told him that she loved him. Otherwise, he was alone; and the loneliness caused more pain than any infection or any physical symptom.

Most will never understand Jay's confusion during those first months of his illness. How could God use him in any way now that he was a "dirty" vessel? His anger, bitterness. and resentment grew toward his Savior, the one who led him to Haiti—apparently to be killed through others' sins. Denial and depression were Jay's constant companions through his daily activities.

Finally, though, God seemed to shout louder than his self-pity.

The Associated Press put out a story about the drug problem in New York City, describing thousands of addicts to heroin, crack, and sex who roamed the streets like sheep without a shepherd. The story impressed Jay's mind. Then an idea clicked. *They need a pastor. Maybe I never shot up like they did, but I am living with the same consequences: AIDS.* Jay felt as if God were speaking directly to him, calling him to the streets of New York.

But Jay never had the opportunity to make it to his mission field. About eight months before he was scheduled to graduate from school with a master's degree in Christian counseling, Jay was admitted to the hospital with a temperature of 105 degrees. Within two hours he was dead from his final bout with pneumonia.

Sue

Six months had passed since her husband Ernie had died, and Sue had been left alone to care for their two early-teens children. But she was also sick, and soon was admitted to the hospital with severe headaches, the inability to walk, and a high fever. She knew what she had, and she knew that eventually she would die.

The reason for her dying needed to be publicized because so few people in 1986 knew that AIDS could be spread heterosexually. So Sue agreed to tell her story to a major publication, making sure the article would not be published until after she died.

Sue's story began with Ernie, who had been a typical business salesman. He was attending a convention in Philadelphia in late 1984 when he went out drinking with a group from his company. On their way back to the hotel they saw a group of adult bookstores along with a large flashing sign for "Peep Shows." Some of the group members were familiar with the shows, and had stopped to partake.

On a dare, good old faithful Ernie, the man who had never cheated on his wife, was chided into viewing a "peep" show after his colleagues told him some half-truths. He ended up having sex with a prostitute.

The guilt was tremendous at first, but his friends urged him to put it out of his mind so that his wife would not get suspicious. He had never told Sue about that episode—until he was dying of AIDS.

Almost two years after the convention, both Ernie and Sue had accepted Christ as their Savior in a Christian and Missionary Alliance Church that was near their home. With the counsel and discipling of their pastor, the children also became believers and often attended church. With no symptoms of any health problems, neither Sue nor Ernie had any idea that they were ill.

However, just as their spiritual conversion occurred, their health complications and problems seemed to begin. Within five months, Ernie was reduced from a robust 210-pound frame to 117 pounds. He suffered a number of infections that sapped his energy, his strength, and his flesh. Yet Ernie refused to tell Sue that the underlying cause for his decay was not the infections, but AIDS. Because Sue had no symptoms, he thought his wife was safe.

13

The secret was kept until the last week of Ernie's life. Sue learned then because the physician suggested so strongly that she needed to be tested. She not only found out how Ernie contracted AIDS, but three days later found out that she was also infected.

During their time of illness, this Christian couple was loved by their pastor and a few of their closest friends. Help around the house, the running of errands, prayers, cards of remembrance, flowers, and food were all given as help in their time of need. But many in their church did not understand about AIDS. They broke fellowship with Sue and Ernie, and eventually left that church for another, erroneously believing they were at risk of personally contracting AIDS from Sue and Ernie.

But Sue loved them anyway. She wrote them, called them, and tried to express Christ's love, even when they shunned her attempts. It was because of her love for these people, because of the naive attitudes of some Christians, and because of the lack of publicity about heterosexual spread of the disease that Sue felt her story needed to be told.

Ernie died about eight months before his wife. The issue that contained their testimony and story outsold every other national newspaper that day. Their children are free from the disease and are growing up with their grandparents; they have not been told why their parents died of AIDS.

Terry

Terry often said he would rather live any life instead of his own. Abused sexually as a child, his mother had sold him to other men for sex in exchange for drug money. Then he quickly learned to sell himself to other pedophiles and homosexuals who were looking for "a new face." During his teen years, he survived three gunshot wounds, five overdoses of heroin, two severe beatings, a slashed throat, and a score of auto accidents.

He converted to homosexual practices in his later teen years when he was kicked out by his aunt. Then there were more thrills to be experienced: sex, violence, and drugs all rolled up into one life style. Most of his friends became involved with sadomasochism and Terry gleefully worked to become the most vicious. Following the example of one of his lovers, he became involved with Satan worship, and ceremonies that included human sacrifice, child sex, and human torture. There was no new evil left for Terry to experience.

One of his special homosexual lovers was Billy Joe, for whom Terry believed no gift was too expensive, and no task was too difficult. Nothing was sweeter than "a night out with Billy Joe," according to Terry. But suddenly, Billy Joe disappeared from the night spots and would not answer his phone. No one seemed to know where he had gone.

A few months later, Billy Joe returned to his friends a little changed. He had been admitted to the hospital and diagnosed with AIDS. While he was hospitalized, he had met a burly old man named Robert who was making spiritual rounds in the hospital. Robert shared the gospel and Billy Joe accepted it. He then prayed for strength so that he could go and win his lovers to Christ as well.

Terry talked with him for hours; and when they were done, he began a new life—a changed life. The desire for sex, for drugs, for violence was gone. He immediately went home, shaved, showered, combed his hair without the usual colored mousse, and threw his leather clothing down the trash chute. He went to a local Christian bookstore and bought the largest red Bible he could find. He stayed away from the bars and neighborhoods where he usually met his companions in sin.

Life seemed so livable now. But time passed all too quickly. Soon Terry was admitted to the hospital and diagnosed with cryptococcus meningitis, an infectious manifestation of AIDS. Once discharged he could barely walk. A local AIDS ministry invited him to stay with them. Though he was dying, he shared daily with the other AIDS victims who were at the house. He invited his old lovers and their new lovers to the house for tea so he could share the good news of God's love.

REAL PEOPLE, REAL DISEASE

It may be difficult for many who will read this text to understand the enormity of the tragedy that is looming in American society. Few people are touched by the disease now; it is seen only as statistics occurring in far-off cities. But within a few years, every person within the United States will personally know someone who is infected with, who is dying from, or who is already dead from AIDS. Then all will see, real person to real person, the pain, the suffering, the loss, and the loneliness of AIDS victims. And then the tremendous size of the tragedy will be more fully understood.

Most of us have a natural fear of this disease, no matter if we are lay people, pastors, counselors, nurses, physicians, or family. The previously unknown facts about the disease—how it is spread, who can contract it, how long it will stay silent, where it came from—have kept many of us away from AIDS victims. Consequently, our compassion has been placed on the back burner. Our hearts are cold from fear and ignorance.

But it only takes one personal encounter with a real person with AIDS to melt a fearful heart.

For me, that person was Leon. He was traveling through the heart of Virginia, visiting some of his relatives, when he became quite ill. He developed a fever of 105 degrees and soon was covered from head to foot with painful, blistering sores. When I saw him in the emergency room, Leon was in extreme pain. My tentative diagnosis was disseminated shingles, meaning that Leon's shingles had spread to cover his entire body. Yet I knew he had AIDS.

Leon never had to tell me that he had been using intravenous heroin. His arms were scarred with the typical track marks of an addict. Huge doses of pain medication also seemed to have little or no effect because his body had become accustomed to such large doses of heroin. My suspicions were confirmed by his girlfriend, Roberta. She gave me most of my information about Leon.

Like day and night, Roberta and Leon appeared to be different people from two opposite ends of society. He had grown up in the poor, urban inner city, where drugs, crime, and violence became a means of survival. She came from a conservative, church-going family that lived in a neighboring suburb. Her well-ordered life had been free from the pain that drugs and crime can bring to families. She was attending a local urban university when they met. She needed to rescue someone, and he needed to be rescued.

Roberta often shared her dream of keeping Leon drug free, helping him to maintain a job, and eventually marrying and having children. She maintained her relationship with him, hoping to extract him from the environment that was consuming his very soul. Unfortunately, that relationship was often sexual, confirmed by her references to him as "Leon, the luscious lover."

The more I talked with Roberta, the more I knew Leon, and the more I grew in compassion for him. No longer did fear of the disease force me to see him as a patient held captive in a glass vault. Leon became as real as any of my other patients; he just happened to have a terminal disease. My heart was able to reach out to this man who had so many needs. I could overlook his Job-like appearance, his grotesquely scarred visage, his face and hands oozing from open blisters. I could put aside his past problems and his present addictions to see a human soul who had needs that I could provide. A hand on his shoulder, a warm smile, my presence to listen to his suffering and pain, and a prayer for his healing, all could be given joyfully to a heroin addict from New York City.

Leon had become a real person; the unknown had been smashed.

But within hours of breaking this barrier, he was gone. He left the hospital AMA (against medical advice) so that he could get a fix and decrease his pain. He was gone before we could tell him that his AIDS test was positive. Though I was grateful that he had not died, I grieved that I had lost my first AIDS patient to the addiction that was his master. I grieved as well for Roberta, the rescuer who probably would die from the AIDS infection she would contract from her sexual relationship with Leon in her futile attempt to keep him drug free.

This "AIDS awakening" is a common experience to those who now work actively in caring for or ministering to victims of this dread disease. The initial fear of dealing with the disease is shed after an encounter with a real, human AIDS patient. The fact that people with AIDS are terminally ill makes them even more pitiful and in need of the love, the care, the compassion, and the giving we are able to share with them. I have discussed this emotional stepping stone with a number of people and each has had a similar time of shedding the tough, protective coating, and replacing it with a smooth, tender, and pure skin of compassion. It is easy for an AIDS patient to see and feel the difference.

Any move into the unknown takes a leap of faith, whether it is trusting God for a new ministry or overcoming the fear to hold the hand of an AIDS victim. Moving out of fear-filled complacency into this new and awakened relationship with AIDS victims can only come if and when you have the opportunity to become personally involved with their physical, emotional, and spiritual needs. That first leap of faith is often difficult, but it is exhilarating and rewarding for the brave and faithful.

Learning about the scientific aspects of AIDS, the facts, the myths, the future course, will help you to take your personal leap of faith in ministry to an AIDS person as intelligently and as fearlessly as possible.

CHAPTER TWO

AIDS: THE DISEASE

Jennifer

Sexual activity had been an expected, normal part of high-school life. Between classes, many of the girls gathered in the bathroom, puffing wildly on a cigarette and discussing which of the boys were "good" at sex and why, and if or how they should use condoms. Everyone seemed to talk about sex, brag about it, and enjoy it. How could it be so bad?

For those like Jennifer, a quiet and pretty sophomore, the discussions opened up a whole new world of experience and adventure. By the time she had completed college, she could not count the number of sexual contacts she had had; it was well over one hundred. Birth-control pills were readily available through the local Planned Parenthood, and they appeared willing to help when she became infected with gonorrhea and herpes. They never once told her to consider other possible consequences of her sexual activity.

I first met Jennifer when she was a senior in college. She had a recurrence of herpes and was seeking another prescription for Zovirax, the medication used to prevent the painful sores that spread the disease to others. We talked at length about her sexual life style. Her parents couldn't seem to care less if she was sexually active, as long as she didn't get pregnant. They never talked about sex, relationships, values, or just how to use birth control. From the age of thirteen Jennifer was able to date and stay out until midnight. Communication in the home was poor, and she never felt the "love" of her parents.

"I don't know what you have been told about AIDS, but your life style has put you at risk for catching the virus. I would suggest being tested before you are married in the fall," I said.

"You've got to be kidding," she stated with disgust. "I've never used drugs, been homosexual, given blood, French-kissed a gay man, or traveled outside of the United States. I don't think I need to be tested."

After talking further and showing her some articles about heterosexual spread of AIDS in the United States and Africa, she said she would consider it. Besides believing that giving blood and foreign travel could cause AIDS, she also brought up the subject of mosquitoes as carriers of the disease; and she expressed the belief that only "gay" men could pass it to anyone. She left that day without being tested, but with my last admonition:

"Please don't have sex until you get tested. If you are infected you could infect someone else with a deadly disease," I warned.

She did come back for testing—and she was positive. Fortunately, almost no effects were seen in the other blood testing that suggested even minor problems with her immune system. A regimen of AZT was initiated and we spent almost two hours one day discussing how to protect others and how to keep herself healthy.

"I still can't believe all the lies and half-truths I have been told about AIDS. If I had known about this sooner, I might have stopped having sex; I might never have gotten the disease. And I would never knowingly pass this on to anyone else," she said.

THE AIDS RUMOR MILL

When three factors are present—a deadly disease, an unclear means of spread, and absence of a cure—then myths and rumors have fertile ground to grow and fester. Health professionals often must dispel the myths and rumors about cancer before the patient has a clear understanding of the disease, its course, the prognosis, and the treatments. This same need for accurate information is true for AIDS patients. Magazines, tabloids, and even accepted scientific journals have added to the general rumor mill creating hundreds of pieces of misinformation about this disease.[1] Fears create rumors that foster ignorance that create more fear. Even though the disease is dangerous, people's perceptions of their personal risk are often blown out of proportion.[2]

In addition, the vacillation of the Public Health Service has increased the mistrust in our government as a reliable source of information. It has also driven the masses of information-hungry citizens to a number of self-imposed experts who offer myths, half-truths, lies, and other information tainted with personal biases.[3]

To quell public fears of a raging epidemic, the Public Health Service first declared AIDS a disease of homosexual men.[4] Unfortunately, this initial pronouncement was based on sketchy information. By this point in the epidemic, homosexual victims had developed symptoms of the disease, but the HIV virus had already infiltrated the IV-drug users' community, too, and had begun to spread among sexually promiscuous heterosexuals as well. Government officials also declared that blood transfusions were safe and that health-care workers had nothing to fear. However, when more accurate information became available, each of these "facts" had to be reversed.[5] Even some of the present information is based more on "the desire to keep fear under control" instead of providing full warning to the public about scientific studies. Figure 2–1 shows a chronology of some of these initial pronouncements and when they had to be reversed.

How the Public Health Service and Other
Medical Experts Have Changed Their
Stands on Many Important AIDS Issues

AIDS Issue	Stand Taken
1. AIDS is a disease *only* of homosexual males.	True (Fall 1983) False (Spring 1984)
2. HIV will *never* be spread through blood transfusions.	False (Fall 1983) True (Spring 1984)
3. HIV infection is 100 percent fatal.	False (November 1987) True (August 1988)
4. AIDS can be transmitted by saliva.	False (Fall 1987) True (1989)
5. Inform spouse of HIV-infected patient.	No (January 1988) Yes (January 1989)
6. AIDS will never become a heterosexual problem.	True (1983) False (1987)
7. HIV is "low" risk to health-care workers.	True (January 1988) False (October 1988)
8. All preoperative patients should be tested to allow for increased precautions by physicians and nurses in the operating room.	No (March 1988) Yes (October 1988)
9. All persons should be tested prior to marriage.	Disagree (1987) Agree (1988) (Several states now have laws requiring premarital tests for HIV; others are considering it.)
10. AIDS is a major epidemic spreading throughout the United States and other areas of the world.	False (1985) True (1988)

(Adapted from *AIDS Risks* by Lorraine Day, M.D.)

Figure 2–1

What information is trustworthy? Where can a person go to get the most up-to-date and accurate information? Can people accept the daily news reports about AIDS? Can they believe in the treatments and scientific discoveries that are announced? How do they know which experts are well trained, which are not, and what their biases are? How do we protect our families or our counselors from overly fearful or inadequately emphatic information? How do we sort truth from lies?

STRAIGHT ANSWERS TO AIDS QUESTIONS

The medical diagnosis and treatment of AIDS is relatively easy compared with aspects of counseling AIDS victims and their families. Some of our counseling time must be spent simply sorting truth from myth. A majority of the initial time I spend counseling AIDS patients is used to help them "unlearn" the inaccuracies they have been taught, and then to replace them with more up-to-date scientific information. As a practicing physician, I must also acknowledge the real "doubts" that still exist within our present body of knowledge—areas that need to be answered with "no one knows!"

A counselor's need to know about AIDS is essential. By dealing with some of these myths espoused as truths we can begin to unfold the entire picture of the AIDS epidemic.

How did the epidemic begin?

The most plausible explanation of the origin of this epidemic begins with "Patient Zero," a homosexual man who probably contracted the disease from a sexual contact in Paris. He then is believed to have spread the disease to homosexual groups in Canadian and American cities. Patient Zero was linked to about forty of the first two hundred cases in the homosexual communities of these cities. His story will be told later.

How could Patient Zero spread it to so many people?

The more sexual contacts the patient has, the more likely it is that he or she will catch or spread a venereal disease. This man claimed he had more than two hundred different sexual partners each year; some believe it was closer to five hundred. The type of sexual activities he was involved in, homosexual intercourse, is an efficient way of passing the virus from one person to another.

Are there any other explanations about how it started?

Some scientists disagree with the Patient Zero theory. They believe that the virus has been around for many years, possibly as early as 1960 or so. They also believe the virus has been present in Africa since the 1940s. If everyone who contracts AIDS takes seven to ten years to develop symptoms and die from complications, then these scientists are probably closer to the truth.

However, we know AIDS has been spread in epidemic proportions and we can trace cases to single individuals who were infected. We also know that the more exposure there is to the virus, such as a person who has multiple homosexual partners, the more likely the patient will develop symptoms within the first two to three years. That person is also likely to die more quickly.

The exponential growth, the contact tracing of spread, the number of contacts, and rate-of-death statistics all suggest that AIDS has been spread from a very small number of very sexually active people throughout this country.

Was AIDS created in some government laboratory?[6]

Viruses very similar to the AIDS virus have been found all over the world, primarily in animals. The AIDS virus is part of a larger group of viruses called the retrovirus group.[7] It is true that government labs have been studying the virus; but there is no evidence that the virus that causes AIDS or a mutation of that virus was created in a government or any other laboratory.

This particular myth was started and has been perpetuated by a few suspicious and paranoid persons exhibiting a genre of psychological dysfunction that is fairly common. These people believe that all bad things are created by a sinister government, such as a "communist" government, which doesn't care for its people. This delusion is more common than most people realize. Most physicians and psychiatrists have had to deal with individuals who believe this way.

Can I contract AIDS if I donate blood?

It is impossible, theoretically and practically, to contract AIDS from giving blood. The sterile needles and bags used to collect the blood have never been exposed to the AIDS virus or to HIV-infected blood. Needles are never reused and no transfusions are given to the person donating blood for others.

Can I pick up other types of infections from an AIDS victim?

There is a possibility for an AIDS victim to carry other respiratory diseases, such as tuberculosis, cytomegalovirus (CMV), mononucleosis, and other more minor viral infections. Their weakened immune systems cause these organisms to be more plentiful in secretions and may make it more likely to be spread to other "healthy" persons. I have heard of a few cases where an HIV-infected person was the "probable" cause for a fellow worker's CMV or mono infections, but these are still very few and far between.

DEBUNKING MYTHS AND HALF-TRUTHS

AIDS is a disease solely of homosexual men.

It is true that the disease first started in the promiscuous homosexual community, which is now saturated with the virus. However, the sharing of IV needles quickly spread the epidemic from the homosexual community to the community of addicted IV drug users. Through sexual activity, AIDS then crossed into the community of heterosexual IV drug users. Today, there is a large epidemic raging among heterosexuals. In many large cities, women who have been infected with the disease by their sex partners pass the disease on to their babies.

Thus, AIDS is not just a disease of homosexual men. Sexual behaviors spread the disease, not sexual preference.

If I use protection, such as a condom, I can't get the disease.

Condoms are not an absolute protection against AIDS. The failure rate for condom usage among teen-agers is as high as 75 percent. The accepted condom failure rate among adults is 10 to 15 percent. The term "safe sex," unfortunately, is a half-truth. Protective devices may reduce your risk, but having any sexual activity is thousands of times more risky than another protective behavior: abstinence.

If I test positive, that means I am exposed and will not necessarily contract AIDS.

There is probably no more cruel nor deceptive myth than this to give people a false sense of security. In most cases the term "exposed" was used in ignorance. Early in the epidemic, people who tested positive for the virus were told that they were "exposed." But what did that mean? Had they shaken hands with a person who had AIDS? Had they had sex with a person with AIDS? This myth of "exposure" was one factor in spreading the fear of casual contact. Further, people who had been "exposed" to AIDS and who tested HIV-positive believed they would not get the full-fledged disease.

The truth is this: If an HIV test is positive, it indicates the person is infected with the AIDS virus and can infect others, even though he or she may not have symptoms for years.[8] Those who have a positive test have both the antibodies to the virus as well as the virus in their system. Their "exposure," often through a promiscuous behavior, has resulted in the disease.

Biting insects such as mosquitoes and lice can spread AIDS.

No studies have conclusively proven that biting insects can or will spread AIDS. The Public Health Service has said it will never happen, even when they know infection is still possible, though very unlikely. The problem is simple: Insect spread of AIDS cannot be proven.

The possibility of spread is based on two simple and provable facts. First, any virus that is blood-borne could be transferred from an infected person to a noninfected person. The probability for viral spread through insects increases as the number of infected people increases. Second, the greater the mosquito population, the more likely these diseases are to spread from one infected person to another noninfected person.[9]

The good news is that mosquito control programs have greatly decreased the number of mosquitoes in the United States and greatly reduced the diseases spread by these insects. But there is bad news as well. We will never be able to prove if mosquitoes or other biting insects are carriers, because of the latent period. Would you remember a mosquito bite that happened five to ten years ago? Even if you did, could you prove or disprove that it was that mosquito, that particular mosquito, and not some other insect or activity, that gave you AIDS?

As the population of AIDS patients in Africa reaches 20 percent of some countries, and as mosquitoes are rampant in those countries, it becomes more likely that a small number of persons will contract AIDS through an insect bite. Though this is theoretical, it is a reasonable assumption. Other viral infections, such as yellow fever, are carried by the mosquito. Because a smaller proportion of all American citizens have HIV, approximately 1 percent, and because our mosquito population is much smaller than Africa's, it is unlikely that biting insects will present a risk factor for contracting AIDS now or in the future.

AIDS can be contracted by eating after an AIDS patient, using the communion cup, touching a door handle, or sitting on a toilet seat.

Casual contact will never be a proven route of spread for this disease. The reason is quite simple. Would you remember the public facilities that you used, or the door handles that you touched ten years ago? To be proven, you have to go back to the original suspected source and find the virus. And that will never be possible.

Although it is theoretically possible to contract AIDS from an unclean surface that has been soiled with semen or blood, all studies to date suggest that casual contact is highly unlikely—or possible at such a slow rate that it is almost nonexistent.[10] Your God-given, God-designed bodily defense mechanisms are sufficient to protect you from viruses, bacteria, foreign bodies, and a host of other noxious organisms that are in our environment.

Recent studies also suggest that saliva is not a secretion we must be concerned about. Antibodies, specific proteins that bind and destroy any and all viruses, are found in large amounts in your saliva, and offer protection from passing the virus from someone's mouth to yours.

If I have AIDS, I shouldn't be tested because there is no cure.

Some persons have suggested they would rather not know whether or not they have the virus. They might say, "If I know I am going to die, I'll just worry about it." But science is changing very rapidly. It is wise to be tested, both for yourself and for the safety of others.

Ideally, knowing that you are infected will stop any risky behaviors. Then you should tell all persons with whom you have had contact to be tested as well. Early testing also means early treatment. People live longer and have fewer health problems when they are started on medication early and followed closely by a physician.

FACTS ABOUT AIDS

Almost everyone in the United States has become familiar with basic facts about AIDS. The Surgeon General's campaign to get AIDS information into every household was effective in raising the awareness of millions to basic information about AIDS.[11] Yet I talk with people every day who are still unaware of important pieces of the puzzle. They may know now the virus is passed by sex, but may also consider touching the skin and kissing to be alternate routes of spread. A recent survey of teens demonstrated a great deal of misinformation and misunderstanding was present in their young and impressionable minds.[12] Misunderstandings in this age group are totally unacceptable because teens represent the greatest risk group in the 1990s and beyond.

We all have a long road before us to clear the muddy water of myth from our minds. Because we are likely to be counseling AIDS patients, or talking with their families or friends, it is essential that we have the best and most usable information to date.

There is always speculation in any scientific area, no matter how well proven a given "fact" is. Science is never hard and fast; it is always changing, clarifying, upgrading, and improving. The information presented here will be the most unbiased and forward-looking data that can be found. It will be based on present fact, common sense, and the principles that make any science understandable.

THE AIDS VIRUS

AIDS infections are caused by a virus, a small protein-coated particle that must rely upon other cells to live and multiply. The AIDS virus enters the body and slowly destroys tissues in the immune system and the nervous system.[13] The infecting agent is a retrovirus, initially labeled HTLV III (Human T-Lymphocyte Virus), but now it has been renamed HIV (Human Immunodeficiency Virus).[14] We will use the newer and more accepted abbreviation of HIV interchangeably with the acronym AIDS (Acquired Immunodeficiency Syndrome) throughout this book.

Viruses cannot live without the help of the person, animal, or bacteria they infect. Viruses cannot reproduce themselves; they are dependent upon the cell that they infect to make copies of the virus so that the infection can spread. Bacteria produce toxins and/or invade the cells directly, causing destruction. Viruses are so small they can fit through a keyhole in the cell wall "door" (called a receptor). The virus locks into the receptor and pushes its genetic material into the cytoplasm, the fluid inside the cell. From there, the viral instructions find their way to the nucleus, the cell's control center, splice themselves into the genetic material of the host cell, and take over the cell's machinery. The nucleus, the enzymes, and all the organelles in the cell are now under the control of these viral instructions to reproduce more viral particles. New viral instructions and protein coats are then manufactured until the cell is stuffed full of new viruses. The cell lyses or breaks open, spreading new viruses all over the body.

Cold or influenza viruses are similar. These particles find their way into the nose or mouth of the victim. They attach to receptors on the surface of mucous membrane cells (the cells that line the nose, mouth, eyes, lungs, and stomach). They quickly reproduce in these cells causing many of them to lyse. This leads to redness, soreness, mucous drainage in the nose, throat, etc. The new viral particles are then spread through the blood, as well as up and down the respiratory tract.

Antibiotics are unable to kill cold or flu viruses, leaving our bodies helpless against the uncomfortable symptoms they produce unless we use symptom-relieving medications, such as cold medications, nonaspirin products, and hot liquids—especially chicken soup! Though it may take days, our body's defenses usually catch up with the virus by producing antibodies against it. Antibodies then destroy any new viral particles, stopping the spread of the infection and allowing the symptoms to resolve.

Cold viruses act very quickly, invading cells, reproducing, and lysing the cells within a matter of days. However, the AIDS virus, HIV, enters the cell, slowly reproduces, and destroys strategic cells in the immune system over a period of years. This long latent period, the time between infection and appearance of symptoms, is common for retroviruses and is the most difficult and frustrating part of AIDS infections.[15] Many people will spread the infection before their bodies make antibodies or develop symptoms. The longer the time before symptoms occur, the more possible it becomes to spread the infection to others.

HIV infection also follows a similar infection route as the cold virus, but it enters in other places than the respiratory tract. The HIV virus is passed by sexual intercourse, by blood transfusions, by contaminated needles, and almost certainly by breast milk.[16] In other words, the virus is not passed in respiratory-tract secretions, but in sexual secretions and in the blood (serum-based secretions).

Homosexual intercourse, passing sexual secretions into an inflamed or bleeding rectum, spreads the virus very efficiently from one partner to another. And because homosexual men are very promiscuous, some having as many as five hundred partners per year, it is easy to see how quickly and completely the spread of HIV could occur through the homosexual community. Infected secretions on sore or bleeding tissues are an extremely efficient way to pass the infection.

Intravenous drug users share needles, injecting the illegal drug into their own veins, then passing it to another. They often are very promiscuous sexually as well. This double exposure has allowed HIV infections to run wild in this group of addicted individuals. Infected blood on a shared needle is also an efficient way to spread the virus.[17]

Before testing was available in 1984, many units of donated blood were tainted with the HIV virus. It is tragically ironic that hundreds of people became infected with the blood that was given to save their lives.[18] These people were victims of a disease or accident that necessitated a blood transfusion; subsequently they became victims of the sexual or intravenous drug addictions of others as well.

The same can be said for the thousands of hemophiliac children in this country. Hemophilia is a clotting disease where a specific blood factor, Factor VIII, is not produced by the body. This missing factor can be recovered and reinjected to help when hemophiliacs bleed. Factor VIII is found in such small quantities that it is necessary to pool large numbers of blood transfusions to recover enough. Yet 92 percent of these innocent children are now infected with HIV because of their dependence upon Factor VIII from transfusions—the very treatment that has saved most from bleeding to death. Many are now dead and many more will die.[19]

A growing number of individuals have become infected through normal heterosexual activity, some through one episode of intercourse with an infected husband, wife, fiancé, or sexual partner, others through multiple episodes. Many others have or will become infected through their promiscuous sexual activities. Many of these will use condoms or other protection. Yet we have proven one simple but essential piece of information. The more promiscuous you are, the more likely you are to catch the virus. The more exposure you have to sexual secretions, the more likely the virus will enter your body, and slowly but surely destroy your immune system.[20]

The virus, once passed by sexual secretions or by serum-based secretions, finds its way to certain "friendly" cells in the body. On the surface of "friendly" cells, T-lymphocytes, certain nerve cells, macrophages, langerhans cells, and possibly other cells, the HIV particle finds a CD4 receptor. They attach to these receptors and squeeze their instructions into the cell. The viral-protein coating is left behind as the simple RNA-encoded instructions (similar to DNA) make copies of themselves. These copies splice themselves into the genetic instructions of the lymphocyte. Every time that cell reproduces itself in response to an infection, it also reproduces multiple copies of these HIV instructions. A schematic view of this infection process is shown in Figure 2–2.

After the cell has reproduced itself a number of times, something turns on the viral instructions, causing large numbers of these instructions to be made and coated inside the cell. Many scientists believe it is another viral infection, such as CMV or Epstein-Barr, that may start this viral overload. The cell then bursts, showering new HIV particles all over the body.

The HIV virus is very specific for T-lymphocytes because they are covered with CD4 receptors. They attach, enter, and eventually destroy these important cells that guide and direct immune function. The more these cells are destroyed, the less the immune system is able to fight off infections or guard against

Lifecycle of HIV

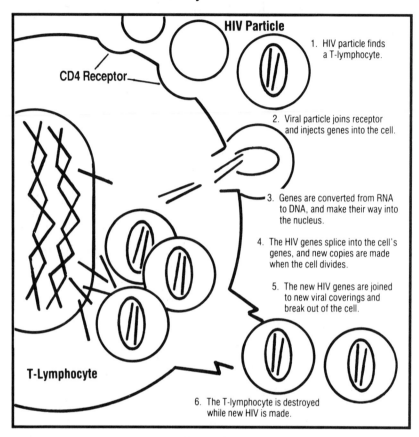

Figure 2-2

newly formed cancers. It takes many months, or even years, for the virus to destroy enough of these T-lymphocytes before symptoms of HIV begin to occur.

Treatments are aimed very specifically at stopping the virus from entering the body (protection), at destroying the virus once it enters the cell (vaccine), or at stopping the virus from entering the cell or making copies of itself (AZT, DDI, and many other medications).

The most effective means of protection is total and complete abstinence from sex or intravenous drugs. The use of condoms may reduce a person's risk, but it also gives him or her a false sense of security: "I can have as many sexual partners as I want if I just use condoms." Since condoms and spermicide are only 85 to 90 percent effective at stopping sperm, a particle much larger than a virus, they are probably even less protective from HIV.

Vaccines are in the developmental stage, and are unlikely to be ready for many years. The presently available treatments, AZT, DDI, and other DNA nucleotide analogs block the progression of the virus within the cell. They block the virus from making copies of itself and from splicing itself into the DNA instructions of the cell. The medications, which often have serious side effects, must be taken every four hours without fail so that the virus doesn't slip though its dragnet. Also, the reports of new strains of HIV that are resistant to AZT, along with the probable further mutations of the virus, will make it more difficult for us to fight the spreading epidemic of HIV.[21]

In summary, the HIV virus is an extremely elusive opponent. Infection with HIV occurs through sexual sharing or contamination with blood products. The virus slips stealthily into the body, finding very specific cells and receptors with which to join. Once inside the cell the RNA viral instructions hide in the genetic material of the cell (DNA). After many months or years, the virus destroys the cell and damages the immune system. Eventually, between two to ten years or longer, the patient will die from infections or cancer because his or her immune system has been decimated. Just as it is with herpes, a nonfatal venereal infection, there is no cure. Unfortunately, HIV kills its victims. However, it kills so slowly that the virus is often passed to many other people before the infected person becomes sick and dies.

THE EPIDEMIC IN THE UNITED STATES

The key problem with this rapidly spreading epidemic is this latent period. It takes so long for symptoms to develop that those who are sexually promiscuous will often spread the disease to scores of partners, and those partners will spread it to scores of others before the first person is afflicted with his or her first symptom. The delay that occurs between the virus entering the body of the victim and the appearance of the first symptoms or signs of illness may be from less than a year to more than ten years. Even when people try to detect the infection early by checking for antibodies against the virus they may fail, because the test doesn't become positive from two months to more than a year after the promiscuous individual contracted the disease.

As mentioned earlier, the start of the disease in this country has been tracked to one specific person in the homosexual community, appropriately named "Patient Zero."

This young, attractive homosexual male airline steward related his story to Researchers for the Centers for Disease Control in Atlanta. His job as an airline steward gave him the privilege of traveling throughout the world. He had traveled extensively throughout Europe, and to Paris, where many of the first cases of HIV infection were seen.[22] The disease appears to have originated in Africa, where European homosexual men traveled for vacations to include sexual promiscuity among their activities.

From the homosexual community in Paris, Patient Zero traveled through Canada, then on to San Francisco, Los Angeles, and many other American cities, including Dallas, Miami, Atlanta, Philadelphia, and New York City. In each of these cities, his numerous contacts with other homosexual liaisons quickly spread the disease to hundreds of young men, who in turn spread it to thousands and tens of thousands.

This airline steward lived for years after being diagnosed as having GRID (Gay-Related Immunodeficiency) or AIDS. Did this stop his sexual contacts? It has been reported that his activities continued, and on occasion, after episodes of anonymous intercourse (common in gay bath houses), he would turn up the lights and show his unsuspecting partner his large dark spots (Kaposi's sarcoma), smugly pronouncing, "I have gay cancer! Maybe you'll get it too!"

Many of these homosexual men did contract HIV infection. Almost all of the early cases of HIV can be traced to "Patient Zero" or someone who had sex with him. Most of them are now dead.

That's how the epidemic got started, and how it spread so quickly through the homosexual community.

How did it break out of this community and infiltrate the IV-drug and the heterosexual communities? Simply enough, some homosexual men spread the disease to others by using IV drugs, female prostitutes, and having sexual contacts with the opposite sex. Many married, bisexual men live with a female marriage partner, but have affairs with homosexual men. They have infected their innocent wives, who knew nothing about the homosexual activities.[23]

Men with serious sexual addictions to pornography and to sexual gratification through use of prostitutes may also use homosexual contacts to gratify their immense sexual appetites. In fact, these three groups are responsible for spreading HIV from one corner of the United States to the other: promiscuous homosexual men, IV drug users, and heterosexual addicts. All are so addicted to fulfilling their own lusts and desires that they are unable to change or modify their sexual behavior. These addicted men, and the smaller number of heterosexually addicted women, are controlled so strongly by their habits that they have lost their sense of judgment and their ability to make healthful decisions. That is why HIV should be called a disease of "addiction."

The epidemic continues to spread through male, homosexual IV drug users, and sexual addicts, and now is advancing down the avenue of heterosexual promiscuity. Heterosexual men and women have become infected through one or more sexual episodes with those "addicts." But now the disease has jumped from addicts to "curious" adolescents who are experimenting with their sexuality. A recent study in 1989 showed that three out of one thousand college-aged young people are already infected with HIV.[24] None of these sexually active adolescents had any symptoms. Further studies show that 79 percent of all adolescents have sexual intercourse before marriage.[25]

The threat of AIDS has not yet slowed this promiscuity, or caused these sexually active teens to change their attitudes, or use protection. (See Figure 2–3.) If this continues, the rate of infection will be approximately 2 percent of the United States population by the early 1990s, and 3 to 5 percent by 1995. Remember, very few if any will have symptoms of illness by 1995 and they are likely to be spreading the disease even further.

Adolescent Sexual Promiscuity: Review of
Statistics for Christian and Secular Young Adults

Secular Studies[1]

1. Young adults who have had intercourse by:
   - Age 15   57 percent
   - Age 19   79 percent
2. Teens who have sex once a month to once a week:
   - Age 15   33 percent
   - Age 19   52 percent
3. Teens who use contraceptives:
   - Age 15   60 percent
   - Age 19   58 percent
4. Young adult males who have had intercourse by:
   - Age 15   60 percent
   - Age 19   88 percent
5. Young adult women who have had intercourse by:
   - Age 15   20 percent
   - Age 19   60 percent
6. Percentage of young women who will become pregnant by the time they marry or are age 19:
   - 25 percent
7. Young adults who believe abortion is the best solution to pregnancy:
   - Age 15   56 percent
   - Age 19   50 percent
8. Percent of sexually active teens who know that AIDS can be spread heterosexually:
   - Age 15   96 percent
   - Age 19   99 percent
9. Percent of teens who say AIDS has caused them to change their sexual behavior:
   - Age 15   26 percent
   - Age 19   15 percent
10. Percentage of parents who teach their children about sexuality.
    - 1965   5 percent
    - 1988   39 percent

Christian Studies[2]

1. Percentage of Christian young adults who have engaged in heavy petting or sexual intercourse by age 19: 70 percent
2. Percentage who have engaged in oral sex by age 19: 62 percent
3. Percentage of Christian young women pregnant by age 19: 18 percent
4. Percentage of parents who teach their teens about sexuality.
   - 1985   20 percent
   - 1990   40 percent

References

[1] David Van Biema, "What's Gone Wrong with Teen Sex?" *People Magazine* Poll, 13 April 1987; newspaper articles from 1988–1989, including a poll in *USA Today*; and statistics based on population, age-related pregnancy, and abortion numbers.
[2] Josh McDowell, *What I Wish My Parents Knew about My Sexuality* (San Bernardino, Calif.: Here's Life Publishers, Inc., 1987), 14–15; calculations based on sexual activity, pregnancy rate, and population statistics; and unpublished studies of Christian youth, parenting.

Figure 2–3

These young adults, who seldom use protection, are promiscuous in spite of AIDS, and probably will be dying or dead by the year 2000.

THE FUTURE EPIDEMIC OF AIDS

The future of this epidemic has the potential of becoming the "Black Death" of the twenty-first century. Records show that one-fourth of the population of Europe died in the thirteenth century, and ten million persons died in the Indian epidemic of the late 1800s. AIDS has this same potential for death and destruction.

Within the first ten years of the epidemic the disease was spread from one solitary promiscuous patient to more than 1.5 million persons in the United States, with some estimates as high as 3 million. While the first 100,000 are dying with full-blown AIDS, as many as 900,000 by some estimates have early symptoms of HIV disease, and many more have no symptoms.

Babies are being born with HIV who will not live past their fifth birthdays.

In Africa, the epidemic began in the 1950s or 1960s and has been spread by heterosexual activity, homosexual activity, non-sterilized needles, unscreened transfusions, and from mother to child. Many other countries in the world are also reporting rapid spread of the epidemic to their populations.

Future projections of those infected with HIV are extremely grim. (See Figure 2–4.) Hopefully, the educational campaigns sponsored by many groups in this country and the World Health Organization in other countries will begin to slow the course of this epidemic within ten to twenty years.

Remember, though, that those who have sex and contract the disease today will not have symptoms for five to ten years. Our efforts to slow the disease now are affecting the epidemic ten years from now.

The epidemic in the United States is alive and thriving while the Public Health Service and the media both remain quiet, not desiring to cause panic.

Shouldn't we as responsible citizens do more to warn the millions of young people who are contracting HIV today? Isn't it our responsibility to raise the awareness of our patients to the

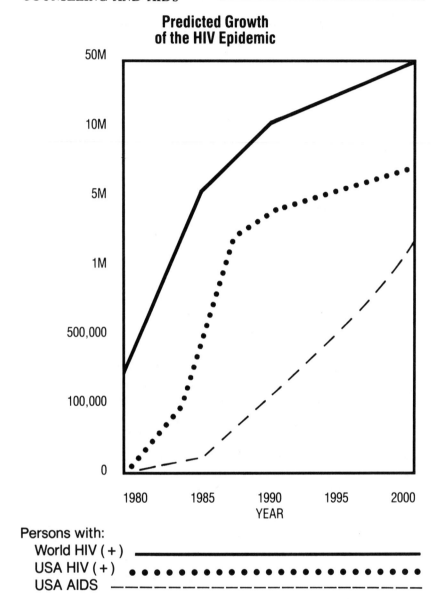

**Predicted Growth
of the HIV Epidemic**

Persons with:
World HIV (+) ————————————
USA HIV (+) •
USA AIDS — — — — — — — — — — — — — — — — — — —

Figure 2-4

dangers of promiscuous sex and drug addiction? Shouldn't our churches become more involved in fighting for the health, the lives and the souls, of our youth?

Helping, counseling, and educating are the tasks each of us can undertake to slow the tide of this disease. Our next chapter will examine the ways HIV affects the lives of our patients and their families. These effects will determine how we can best accomplish the goals of bringing knowledge and comfort to the infected and to the many we are called to protect.

CHAPTER THREE

AIDS: THE EFFECTS

Billy Joe

Going into his seventh week in the hospital, Billy Joe lay motionless in his bed, staring at the blank TV screen on the wall across the room. This hospital stay seemed like an eternity. The physicians had treated him with a number of experimental medications along with Pentamadine and Bactrim because his pneumocystis pneumonia was not responding well.

His problem was first suspected in the fall of 1987. That was when the STD clinic suggested to Billy Joe that he be tested on a regular basis for HIV. He was a fairly regular attendant in the clinic; in fact he had been treated almost a dozen times for herpes, gonorrhea, and Gay Bowel Syndrome. A number of

B.J.'s homosexual partners were also regulars. On that visit, a number of his lymph nodes were enlarged, and he had been chilling and sweating at night. That time, B.J.'s blood test for HIV was negative; but it was a reprieve that would last for only another month.

When he returned in December, he still had enlarged lymph nodes, still had the night sweats, had lost about twenty pounds, had developed a coarse cough and was expectorating foamy sputum. A chest x-ray showed pneumonia on both sides of his lungs. This time when the blood testing was repeated for HIV, it produced a different result: positive. Cultures showed he had contracted "AIDS pneumonia." What was suspected two months earlier was now a surety, and he was hospitalized. It was during this hospitalization that B.J. was reborn to new spiritual life.

If there were ever a patient who received a new lease on life after a serious illness, it was Billy Joe. Not only was a truly new life manifested by his changed desires, motives, and attitudes, but his energy level, his radiant complexion, and his boyish exuberance engendered a portrait of excellent physical health. He had regained about fifteen pounds on his thin frame while he was in the hospital. These factors combined to give him such a healthy appearance that his friends could not believe the news, even from his own lips: "I'm dying of AIDS."

A regimen of medications was given to him for both current treatment and prevention of further infections. For the first twenty months of medical care, which included medication every four hours around the clock and blood tests every month, he experienced only one serious infection. The skin on the left side of his chest had begun to tingle, then sting, then burn intensely. A red streak became filled with painful, pus-filled blisters that soon broke open. The shingles were immediately treated with oral medications, yet they seemed to spread to other areas of his baby-like complexion. After about ten days, the irritation and rash began to fade; but shooting, knife-like pains still raced across his chest like shocks. His physician said they might last as long as he did.

Other than the shingles infection, Billy Joe had very few problems with the disease or his medications. Good health followed him until February 1990. At first, only a few people noticed when B.J. started to be very forgetful. Simple tasks that were part of his normal job were forgotten, and he became very defensive, angry, and out of sorts. People at church were concerned because they had not seen him for three weeks. One night, about 11 P.M. he was found cowering in a alcove near the restrooms at the mall. The sum of his explanation was, "they are going to kill me." That was the beginning of his last hospitalization, which lasted seven weeks.

The police brought him to the emergency room, where he was quickly processed for a "mental-health commitment." The first few days in the psychiatric unit brought injection after injection to help him stay calm and to relieve the paranoia. He developed a cough and fever, along with rapid weight loss, and testing showed a serious pneumonia. B.J. then was transferred to the medical unit of a nearby hospital. When the physicians there found out he was HIV positive, he was transferred again to a larger teaching hospital for treatment in the AIDS center.

Few of his friends even knew he had AIDS and some of those abandoned him. Only his pastor and roommate knew of his admission to the teaching hospital. There, a burly, broad-shouldered man with a deep voice entered B.J.'s room.

"How ya feelin', Brother?" Robert bellowed with his rumbling voice.

B.J.'s mind was so clouded and his strength so little that a response seemed next to impossible.

"Don't ya remember me? I'm the one that led you to the Lord and gave you those books on how to grow," Robert reminded him.

When Billy Jo looked at Robert his gaze seemed to pass right through him. There was no answer.

"I just wanted to let you know that I love ya and I'm praying for ya every day. Jesus loves ya, too!" Robert said.

The expression on B.J.'s face never changed. But finally his eyes focused on the eyes of the big man and tears started to well up. Robert squeezed his hand while he recited a short prayer for strength and healing; then he quietly left the room.

Later that evening, Billy Joe went home to be with his Savior.

His fever climbed to 106 degrees; he had seizures for about five minutes, relaxed, and then calmly stopped breathing.

THE PHYSICAL CHANGES OF HIV

Many HIV patients suffer with Pneumocystis carinii pneumonia, psychiatric disease, and shingles, just as Billy Joe did. A majority of the physical changes and symptoms arise from the destruction of the immune system or destruction of tissues within the nervous system.

Most patients who contract HIV infections will not have any symptoms or bodily signs of infection for an average of seven to ten years.[1] The time from the moment of infection through a sexual act or use of an infected needle to the time of first symptoms is called the asymptomatic period. Since the moment of infection, the viral particles have been entering and destroying, very slowly and very quietly, many of the T-lymphocytes and nerve cells that have CD4 receptors on their surfaces. We can detect changes in the T-lymphocyte counts months to years after infection by assay methods, yet the patient still may not exhibit symptoms of the disease. We believe that other "coinfections," other viral or venereal infections, cause HIV to become very active and destroy cells at an accelerated rate.[2]

The first symptoms noticed by the patient may be a flu-like illness, with sore throat, swollen lymph nodes, fever, aches, and some mild weight loss. The swollen lymph nodes, weight loss, and night sweats may continue for weeks to months, necessitating a visit to the physician for proper diagnosis. Simple infections may be excessive or very prolonged. Simple skin infections may last months. Fungal infections of the mouth or skin may crop up and not depart. Respiratory infections such as mononucleosis and CMV are common and normally linger for eight to twelve weeks—longer in an HIV patient. Tuberculosis is becoming more common in HIV-infected patients as well.

The symptoms that are of greatest concern are the more serious infections and cancers that occur when the immune system is almost completely destroyed by the virus. Opportunistic infections, such as disseminated CMV, shingles, toxoplasmosis, yeast infections, cryptococcus, and other non-tuberculin mycobacteria infections are seen in the later stages of immune system destruction. During this stage, cancers such as Kaposi's sarcoma, lymphoma, and others are seen as well.[3] The gradual downhill progression of the disease offers experts a very bleak picture of the epidemic without better and more effective treatments.

To help classify patients and to aid in the understanding of the course of AIDS, a scoring system has been developed at Walter Reed Hospital that describes these effects of HIV and their approximate time period. (See Figure 3–1). In juxtaposition, we have placed the older, less used AIDS/ARC (AIDS Related Complex) classification for comparison. Either scoring system can be explained to the layperson in very simple terms: the more T-lymphocytes destroyed, the more chance for infections and cancer, and the higher the score or grade.

Billy Joe's example offers a descriptive look at the progression of symptoms from initial infection to mortal illness. Just after

Staging of HIV Disease
Walter-Reed Staging
Compared with AIDS/ARC Staging

Walter-Reed	Clinical Symptoms	AIDS/ARC
WR Stage 0	No symptoms, HIV test negative	HIV Negative
WR Stage 1	No symptoms, HIV test positive	HIV Positive
WR Stage 2	Swollen lymph nodes, fever T-helper cell number over 400/mm^3	HIV Positive
WR Stage 3	Swollen lymph nodes, fever T-helper cell number less than 400/mm^3	HIV Positive
WR Stage 4	Swollen lymph nodes, fever, reduced immune function to skin testing	HIV Positive
WR Stage 5	Oral Candidiasis, swollen lymph nodes loss of immune response to skin tests	ARC
WR Stage 6	Opportunistic infections, oral candidiasis, Kaposi's sarcoma, cancers, complete loss of immune function	AIDS
Death		

Adapted from: *AIDS: Information for the Practicing Physician*, American Medical Association, 1 (July 1987): 9; and R. Redfield, et al., "The natural history of HTLV/III-LAV infection," Second International Conference on AIDS, Paris, June 1986.

Figure 3–1

infection, he noticed a flu-like illness with fever, swollen lymph nodes, diarrhea, and some weight-loss. As this was so similar to other illnesses, he didn't even think twice about seeking medical attention. He just rode it out.

B.J.'s case is similar to those of many AIDS victims. The symptoms are so minimal for so long, often two to five years, victims commonly do not seek HIV testing or medical help in any way. During this time the T-lymphocyte counts are dropping slowly, and the patient may notice some weight loss, swelling of the lymph nodes, and night sweats which correspond to Walter Reed (WR) stages 1 and 2.

As the T-lymphocyte count drops farther, other simple infections may occur, but they are more severe and prolonged than usual. HIV-positive adults will contract simple infections, such as herpes simplex, shingles, candida (yeast), or CMV infections, but they will last for weeks to months, and will usually be much more severe than in non-HIV patients because of the partially destroyed immune system.[4] Now, when a physician diagnoses a prolonged case of any of these infections he or she will follow the patient carefully, often suggesting testing for HIV if the infection persists longer than normal. For many AIDS patients, oral candidiasis or chronic CMV infection brings their whole world crashing down around them because they find out they are positive for HIV.

The length of time between stages varies from patient to patient. Billy Joe progressed from infection without symptoms (WR stages I to II) to brain changes, pneumocystis pneumonia, and death (WR stages V to VI) in a matter of two to three years. Jay, the young man mentioned in chapter 1, progressed from a needle stick in 1979 to death in 1989, a full ten years. Billy Joe's infection came through multiple sexual contacts and homosexual activities, including rectal intercourse; thus he exposed himself to large quantities of the virus many times. Jay's infection was probably contracted with very few viral particles introduced by one solitary needle stick. By these examples, we can understand another simple principle: the more virus that is introduced, the more destruction of the immune system, and the sooner the death. The smaller the number of viral particles, the longer it will take the patient to destroy his or her immune system, and the longer it will take before the patient dies.

Do all HIV patients die of the disease? Most projections show that close to 100 percent of those infected with HIV will eventually die of the disease or its complications—some within a few years, most within ten to twenty years.[5] Without vaccines to hasten prevention, without more effective blocking agents to prevent absorption, and without more effective treatments for those infected, the outlook will remain bleak.

NERVOUS SYSTEM SYMPTOMS AND EFFECTS OF HIV

Even though the epidemic began in the late 1970s, it took until the early 1980s for scientists to see direct effects from HIV infection on the nervous system, causing neurological and psychiatric symptoms and disease.[6] The connection between HIV infection resulting in nerve damage was difficult to make. In fact, HIV disease had to be present with psychiatric symptoms as well as neurological damage before epidemiologists and infectious disease specialists could prove the connection. Once they understood that HIV disease destroys nerve cells along with immune system cells, physicians could be on the lookout for young patients who presented with new psychiatric disease as their first symptom of AIDS.

Billy Joe's psychiatric symptoms originated from the damage that occurred to specific areas of the brain. The psychiatric symptoms that Billy Joe had progressed quickly from forgetfulness to errors in judgment to paranoid psychosis. More commonly, HIV patients present symptoms of dementia or senility. These include losses in memory, errors in judgment, and lapses in orientation, finally ending in losses of reality.[7] Anxiety, depression, irritability, and other emotional symptoms are common as well. HIV dementia is classified as a pre-senile dementia, as it progresses quickly and occurs when the patient is young.

The exact reason why HIV patients are afflicted with the dementia is unknown. We believe there is direct destruction of nerve cells that contain CD4 receptors, but there is also destruction of brain tissue from infection of the brain and spinal cord. Many questions need to be answered more completely. Then better treatments for this syndrome can be devised.

Michael

Michael was pacing the fathers' waiting room when he heard "code blue, labor room six" announced on the public-address system. He gasped as he realized that was the room where his wife had just delivered a beautiful baby girl. The doctor spoke to Michael through the intercom. "The baby is fine. But your wife is having some bleeding," he said. This was meager reassurance for any nervous new father. Then the code blue had been called—and Michael had dropped down on his knees to pray.

After about thirty minutes the physician came to the waiting room. "Your wife didn't seem to respond to the Pitocin we first gave her, and she lost a lot of blood. Her blood pressure dropped so quickly that we called for extra help, for oxygen and for extra unmatched blood. She is awake and doesn't seem to have any neurological damage, but she could get some reactions from the blood we had to give her," the physician said.

Eventually, the crisis ended, and both mom and baby did fine. They were home in five days after a much-needed rest from the excitement of delivery. Breast feeding seemed to agree with little Alison; she grew quickly and had no health problems.

Three years later, another blessed event occurred, this time without the hoopla, fanfare, and sirens. A boy was born to the happy family. But the happiness turned to concern two years later when Alison started having problems with speech, standing, walking, and holding things. After a great deal of negative tests, the physicians asked for blood from Alison and her mother. Both were HIV positive. Further testing revealed that both Michael, Sr. and Michael, Jr. were infected as well.

Both parents were started on AZT after some initial checking of the white blood cell counts. No medications, however, were approved for the children. Alison's nervous system steadily and slowly degenerated, stealing her coordination for walking, then making her unable to feed herself. Finally, it destroyed the central portion of her brain to the point where she stopped breathing.

47

Michael, Jr. contracted oral candidiasis and pneumocystis pneumonia. He has not grown now for almost two years but has remained healthy otherwise. A new protocol did become available for testing AZT on children Michael, Jr.'s age, and he was fortunate to be enrolled.

CHILDREN AND AIDS

The tragic story of this family has been told all over the country to try to stimulate donations for drug testing in children with HIV, the group of innocent victims that continues to grow daily. Most of these children were infected in the uterus; a small percentage, like Alison, were infected through the infected mother's breast milk.

After being rescued from bleeding to death with an HIV-infected transfusion, Alison's mother, Beth, now had to see her daughter die, watch as her son was slowly dying, and possibly live with the fact that her children and her husband all would die before she, herself, dies from AIDS.

In New York City, one out of every sixty-one newborns is born with AIDS, and this percentage is growing steadily.[8] Because a child has a 25 percent to 50 percent chance of becoming infected in the womb if his or her mother has HIV, that means between one in fifteen to one in thirty pregnant women in New York City are HIV positive. Because of the disease, many of these precious babies will die before their second birthday. Some estimates suggest that by the year 1991, twenty thousand babies will be infected in the United States through mothers who contracted the disease through drug addiction or sexual contact.[9] In comparison with 1.5 million abortions per year, this number appears quite small. Yet the emotional damage and pain inflicted upon the family continues to build as fears of losing both the child and the mother increase with each passing day.

When it occurs in children, AIDS presents itself differently than in adults. Many children fail to grow and develop normally. Their immune systems fail to fight against viruses such as CMV, mononucleosis (Epstein-Barr), and herpes simplex, as well as tuberculin-like bacteria, fungal elements such as cryptococcus and candidiasis, and of course, Pneumocystis carinii,

48

the commonest infection seen in **AIDS**. CMV infection may be the reason for slow growth. Some children develop destruction and degeneration of their nervous system, and some scientists postulate the cause is either direct destruction of the nerve cells by **HIV**, or by other infections such as cryptococcus meningitis or herpes encephalitis (inflammation of the brain or its coverings). Children with **AIDS** are prone to diarrheal illnesses that are chronic and recurrent, including serious bacterial intestinal infections with salmonella.[10]

As described earlier, **AIDS** can be transmitted to children within the womb, by breast milk, or through transfusion of blood or of Factor VIII (to hemophiliacs). We must remember and be sensitive that all children who have **AIDS** will not have a mother with the same disease.

It is sad that the innocent have to be afflicted with this disease. But a young child may be the product through conception of an immoral and promiscuous act. For years, we have seen the maimed bodies of children born to a mother infected with one or more venereal diseases. Now that antibiotics and good medical care often prevent these destructive infections, the sin still remains. In the case of **AIDS** and children, Scripture rightfully suggests that God will be "punishing the children for the sin of the fathers to the third and fourth generation . . ." (Exodus 20:5).

HEALTH-CARE WORKERS AND AIDS

Fortunately, casual and close contact do not spread HIV from one infected person to another, as explained later in chapter 5. (See Figure 5–1). People who do not have HIV should have virtually no fears about contracting the disease unless they have sex with an infected person, inject intravenous illicit drugs, or become infected through a transfusion. Health-care workers, however, must daily deal with the risk of needle sticks and the fact that HIV-infected persons are often admitted to the hospital. Multiple needle sticks and many HIV-infected patients make nursing, hospital laboratory work, and surgery risky work.

Some early studies showed that health-care workers accidentally punctured by a needle after the needle had been used on an HIV patient had less than a 1 percent chance of contracting

HIV. This is good news for the majority, but the situation still creates a risky work environment.

I know from personal exposure to surgeons that HIV is a real and serious concern. When a patient has any orthopedic (bone) surgery, the surgeon may puncture his gloves two to three times per operation, and have to change gloves. Somewhere between once and twice a week, the surgeon will cut himself through the glove, puncturing the skin and causing bleeding. Somewhere between twenty-five to fifty times per year an orthopedic surgeon is risking infecting himself with HIV. Is there any wonder why a physician would want to know which of his or her patients are HIV positive?

Giving medical care is becoming safer with new masking and protective technologies. But until the risk disappears, many surgeons, nurses, and laboratory technicians will and should take whatever precautions necessary to protect themselves from infection, easing their minds and preserving their families. We will discuss more about the ethics of giving or refusing to give health care in chapter 5.

Jerry

The hustling and glittering life style of Los Angeles gave Jerry a real sense of excitement, a real purpose for living. The Iowa farm belt had never given him any direction. All he saw were the endless seasonal changes, the endless fields of grain, and a life that was being destroyed by boredom. In the fall of 1984 he packed his Macintosh computer into a 1968 Volkswagen bus and moved to the capital of excitement to pursue a career in acting or advertising.

The computer skills Jerry picked up at the local technical college proved invaluable. He immediately got a job with data entry at a large financial institution and quickly moved up the department ladder to become manager of programming. It was not only a hobby and interest for him; his talent for the job was obviously immense when it came to finding solutions for programming problems.

His first apartment quickly gave way to a modern furnished beach-front condominium. To help share payments and other costs, Jerry's girlfriend moved in. Both of them were so busy with jobs, acting classes, auditioning, and tracking down potential opportunities that they never talked about themselves or their relationship. The only time they spent together was in a common bedroom. Their uncomfortable but mutually gratifying sexual relationship, along with their mutual incomes, kept them together until "terrific Teri" walked out to seek a "less boring" relationship. The roommate gap was quickly filled by two friends Jerry met at work.

The sexual preferences of his new male roommates were well known to him.

Through the years Jerry's various heterosexual relationships had been either too standoffish or too sexual. His few homosexual encounters and use of homosexual pornography did not create the same discomfort and heartache as his hetero-heartthrob Teri, and they did offer the same sexual thrills. It was almost as if he was making a statement of sexual preference when his new roommates moved in: "No more girls; let's bring in the boys."

Within six months Jerry and his roommates had increased their sexual activity from minor sexual contact with pornography in the condominium to visits to the gay bathhouses all along the California coast. He had used enhancing drugs, had been involved with violent sex, and had picked up a number of the "gay" diseases. That level of sexual activity and homosexual life style persisted for the next twelve months until Jerry was diagnosed with oral candidiasis—and AIDS. His roommates, who remained lovers during their stay in the condominium, moved out to find "healthier accommodations." They refused to be tested, because they didn't want to know and didn't want to change.

As might be imagined, Jerry was emotionally crushed and became despondent. When he called his parents and told them that he was infected with HIV, their response was simple: "It was your choice and you screwed it up. We don't want to hear from you again!" Jerry hoped they would change their minds after he sent them some materials about homosexuality from the local AIDS Support Network, but they never called or wrote. His ex-girlfriend was happily co-habitating with a "working actor," and never bothered to return his calls.

Fortunately, his physical health did not deteriorate much. Instead, his mental health was the problem.

The initial rejection and loneliness devastated him. The reality of a terminal illness created confusion, grief, and symptoms of reactional depression. But these were immediately compounded by the rejection of his roommates, his ex-girlfriend, and his previously supportive parents. He stayed away from his job for three weeks, crying and walking the beaches. The bottles of tranquilizers looked so inviting: it would be such an easy way to go. *They'll care more when I'm gone,* he thought. But he was never able to muster the courage.

When he returned to work, he sought the help of the company health director, who suggested he receive counseling from a local psychiatrist who dealt with a large number of homosexual clients. The company physician also prescribed an antidepressant and encouraged him to keep busy at work. In addition, he also encouraged Jerry to be sexually responsible and always carry a condom with him. But his advice fell on deaf ears. Jerry went back to the gay bathhouses a number of times after he was diagnosed with AIDS, not out of desire, but out of habit. The glitter of "gay sex" faded quickly, however.

The psychiatrist seemed to offer little help except medication. The counseling sessions uncovered some of the psychological and emotional traumas and relationships that apparently led to Jerry's homosexual introduction and later addiction. But the psychiatrist never attempted to repair or to recover the psychological pieces. He just listened, affirmed Jerry's homosexual urges as a normal variant, and gave him a new prescription with each visit. The medications just complicated his confused emotions, calming them until the next dose.

The third antidepressant seemed to work the best. Then Jerry was finally able to sleep through the night without waking in a cold sweat from recurrent "hospital/mortuary" nightmares. He stopped trying to find a new roommate, fearing rejection once AIDS was discussed. The crying episodes during the evening hours were interspersed with daydreams of bargaining with God for another chance. Almost every episode ended with chest pain, shortness of breath, and tingling in both hands—symptoms of hyperventilation. Then he would take a few "nerve pills" to make sure these symptoms would stop, and then fall asleep about thirty minutes later.

The emotional vacillation continued for two more months. The depressed feelings were uncontrollable. Once, when Jerry had taken an extra antidepressant along with two "nerve pills," his judgment was clouded but he knew exactly how fast he was going and what he was attempting to do when he hit the concrete roadway pillar. Though he would survive this attempted suicide, Jerry died about three months later from a bout of pneumonia.

The Emotional Devastation of AIDS

Maybe Jerry's emotional turmoil would have been less severe if he had made a spiritual commitment; maybe it wouldn't. Nevertheless, he demonstrated many of the emotional responses seen in HIV patients, responses that are as unique as each person with AIDS.

The emotional stresses of AIDS often uncover the base personality characteristics of the patient, testing his or her spiritual resolve to the limit. The persons who are actively pursuing homosexual life styles or who are addicted to intravenous drugs are aware that AIDS is a possible penalty for their actions. Yet denial still runs rampant; they believe it will happen to someone else.[11] Especially when the early symptoms for AIDS are found, such as Jerry's case of thrush (oral candidiasis), the denial wheels begin to turn. Denial is often so strong that patients will not seek help for even severe infections because they don't want to face a possible diagnosis of AIDS.

The emotional reactions to AIDS, and thus our strategies for counseling, fluctuate with the timing of the infection as well. Jerry and others like him were so enthralled with their exciting and sexually satisfying habits that the fear of contracting HIV was of minimal concern. The greater the level of addiction, the more the individual will deny the consequences of his or her addiction. Thus, during the period when a patient is partaking of risky behaviors, denial is the primary defense used to protect their emotional stability.

A one-question method of detecting addiction, and the severity of that addiction, is to query the patients about consequences of addictive behavior and observe how strongly they deny possible problems (i.e., "Do you think your sexual activity could lead to a venereal disease like AIDS?"). It is easier than asking how much and what types of sex it takes for them to be satisfied, which is the emotional/physical gauge for strength of addiction.

When the disease is suspected, denial usually increases until the point of confirmation of the diagnosis. Then a host of emotional reactions can surface. Denial is still the most protective defense and the one most commonly used after AIDS is discovered by blood testing. Shock, anger, resentment, acute reactive depression, panic or other anxiety reactions, guilt, personal bitterness toward the infected lover, even blatant psychoses are possible and observed reactions following a positive test result.[12] These reactions are not dissimilar to emotional reactions seen in other illnesses or terminal diseases; the mental processes are the same.[13]

How did some of the patients described in the first few chapters react to the news that they were positive for HIV?

Jay was shocked and emotionally wrung out when he first learned of his HIV infection through a needle stick during the time he ministered for the Lord in Haiti.

Sue had already worked through her denial, fearing that Ernie's infection could be spread to her. But she could not bring herself to take a blood test until both Ernie and her physician strongly suggested it. She didn't want the children to possibly lose both parents. Her initial reaction was quiet resignation and depression.

Billy Joe knew that he was negative; he believed the positive test must be wrong.

Cese was dumbfounded; she couldn't believe how unfair it was for her to contract AIDS.

Jerry knew he had it as soon as he got the mouth infection. Inwardly, he blamed and resented his roommates because they were the ones who had furthered his addiction. In addition, they were committed to each other rather than to Jerry, even though he paid most of the bills.

These wide swings of emotions are normal for people who are physically ill as they begin to grieve for their loses. The beginning stage of grief is the reaction phase, where the emotions are striking back at the news of impending doom. There are wide variations within this reaction phase, variations in emotions, in time frame, in order, and in the depth of reactions. It is in the acute reaction phase, or in a prolonged, unresolved reaction phase, where counseling can bring the greatest comfort to those suffering loss.[14]

Scripture suggests it is normal and healthy to grieve for our sinful ways, for illness, and for losses of friends or family. (See James 1:2–4, and 5:7–11.) Grief, however, has a natural conclusion, acceptance, and a spiritual purpose, growth.

Our counseling of grieving patients must strive beyond the point of acceptance, reaching deeper into the inner person, bringing forth spiritual fruit, emotional growth, and physical restoration. Grieving patients who doggedly persist in the emotional ocean are tossed to and fro, constantly being exposed to the dangerous elements. We must give them a safe platform within the ocean as well as a map and supplies to chart their way to safety. Too often we offer only the lifeboat, leaving our patients in uncharted waters without a map.

The course to safety through the ocean of emotions depends on the counselor, who must disciple the patient toward acceptance and beyond. When our patients come to the beach of recovery they will be tattered and torn from their trials, but they will have a new confidence and strength to follow God's will for the remainder of their lives.

DEPRESSION AND AIDS

The emotional symptoms of grieving may merge with symptoms of a short-term or reactional depression, or a longer-term or biochemical depression that may require medication. The crying spells, agitation, lack of sleep, and lack of desire to do anything are the common symptoms of all depression. When weeks have passed without signs of resolution, and when the vegetative signs of weight loss, decreased sex drive, inability to concentrate, and early-morning awakening have been added to the above symptoms, then a biochemical depression is probable and medical treatment should be arranged.

Any life-threatening or serious illness can precipitate biochemical depression. Our present theories do not conclusively answer why the emotional stresses of AIDS lead to biochemical changes in the brain neurohormones, the direct cause for biochemical depression, but the likely culprits are the stress hormone system (cortisol and epinephrine) and its effects on the autonomic nervous system.[15] Illness itself, apart from the emotional havoc it causes, creates high levels of biochemical stress through the stress hormones. Whatever the reasons, a person with AIDS may need antidepressive medication along with counseling to relieve the symptoms of depression and to prevent the possibility of suicide.

Another emotional pit is that of anger and bitterness. Once the patient finds his or her way to the bottom of the emotional pit, it is a slow and laborious process of recovery. Those who believe themselves innocently or unfairly infected by another will displace their guilt and pain toward their infected partner. The lack of forgiveness, of personal responsibility, and of purpose for the illness must all be dealt with in what is usually a very slow, releasing process. Anger and bitterness will cause more physical symptoms and problems than denial, repression, suppression, or any other psychological defense because of the high levels of stress hormones and autonomic nervous system activity involved. Truly, the patient hurts himself or herself more than the infected partner by persistent anger or bitterness.

The emotional impact of AIDS encompasses everyone in the patient's support system. The initial epidemic began and spread rapidly through the homosexual community. Thus, lovers and other sexual partners became "family" for the infected person. Within the intravenous drug-using community, traditional families may or may not be present to support the infected drug user. The present silent epidemic and future epidemic, just as in Africa, will be a heterosexual epidemic and will involve traditional family and sexually active teens for the most part.

EMOTIONAL EFFECTS ON SPOUSE OR LOVER

How do you think Carolyn felt when she first heard from her husband, "I'm bisexual and dying with AIDS!" When do you think Sue lost trust in her previously faithful husband? When did Jerry's roommates lose their "love" for him?

There surely is no other disease so difficult for the spouse or lover to deal with than AIDS. In comparison, heart disease is often discovered when a heart attack occurs, usually later in life when disease and degeneration are more expected. Even the ravages of cancer, which rarely affects younger patients, cannot compare with the complicated emotional difficulties of AIDS. Spouses or lovers of AIDS victims often must deal with three separate and serious issues—personal infection with a deadly disease, loss of faithfulness of the sexual partner, and grief for the infected person—each a tragedy by itself.

The sexual partner's grief is greatly compounded when he or she must deal with the reality of his or her own personal infection, and the fear of pain and discomfort from that infection. Counselors must immediately work with spouses or lovers to help them resolve this initial fear. With the accuracy of our present HIV testing, and with the proven benefits of treatment programs for AIDS sufferers, we must suggest testing as soon as possible.[16] It is virtual malpractice to suggest "living with the possibility." The fear of not knowing can be more emotionally damaging than the testing process, especially when a majority of the patients will be negative. Testing resolves the fear of disease for most and will make the few who are positive face the disease sooner and with more hope.

The second issue, that of infidelity, will vary greatly from one relationship to another. Some spouses will show no shock or surprise with the revelation of unfaithful partners because they are in the midst of an equally promiscuous relationship. Others will demonstrate shock, anger, frustration, or denial once they are aware of AIDS in a partner. The scale of their reaction depends upon their level of love, trust, and dependency.

The saddest situation occurs when an extremely dependent wife, who has denied for years that her husband has been sexually active outside of their relationship, becomes aware of her infection with AIDS before it is admitted by her husband. I am aware of such a case involving unresolved denial: The wife denied she could possibly have AIDS and steadfastly refused treatment. The husband left to pursue another relationship.

Finally, the grief a spouse or lover feels for the AIDS victim complicates the other issues. The normally jumbled emotions of grief become tangled with the strong anger aimed at the un-faithful relationship, as well as love for the dying patient. The mixture of hostility, anger, and loving grief can lead to immense confusion that is difficult to sort out within the counseling relationship. Pursuing the positive aspects of their previous relationship and stressing the "no fault" nature of sin may give the grieving spouse or lover a more positive picture of their plight.

Their emotional reactions will hopefully melt into acceptance of God's purpose for illness and continual reliance upon him for growth, comfort, and restoration. Counseling may be necessary when the reactions to illness remain unresolved, especially when the issues of personal infection or unforgiveness for infidelity persist. Dealing with the perceived losses constitutes the primary emotional reactions we must contend with when spouses, lovers, or other family members become involved and are in need of counseling.

FAMILY REACTION TO THE DISEASE

The myths surrounding HIV disease leaves many misconceptions and misinformation in the minds of family members when they hear of a son, daughter, or parent who is afflicted with the virus. One of Jay's concerns was how he could tell his father or grandparents. What would they think of him? He considered it a blessing that his mother had died before he contracted symptoms. "She would have been totally crushed if she knew," Jay had said.

The fear of rejection may drive AIDS patients to wait before telling family members, pushing aside the support they so desperately need. Fortunately, in Jay's case, the fear of rejection from his family did not materialize. Both his estranged father and his loving grandparents grew closer to him and became more supportive as he grew sicker.

Other families are not so understanding. Jerry's family, for example, disowned him. Family members may erroneously believe that all AIDS victims are gay or drug users, even when their relative contracted the disease through heterosexual activity or through blood contamination. They may refuse to listen to other possibilities, even though their rejection is based on false information. Thus, the first step in counseling family members is to make sure they know about AIDS: the science, the effects, and the outcome. Specifics about the AIDS victims' promiscuous behavior can complicate the reconciliation process. However, it may be helpful in rebuilding trust within the family for the infected member to talk briefly and honestly about how he or she contracted the virus. Engaged couples, in this day of HIV, must be more open about previous sexual experiences, or be willing before marriage to take an HIV test to assure the future spouse that he or she will not become infected.

A very serious twist in a family's interactions that greatly complicate both the diagnostic counseling process as well as any treatments is the devastating problem of incest. Sadly, incestuous relationships are more common than previously thought. These illegal and perverse relationships twist how the family reacts when AIDS is discovered in a member. Often the father is driven by pornography to levels of sexual addiction where his judgment is seriously impaired. The possibility of a father infecting his wife and daughters is becoming more and more possible; and with the continuing spread of pornography to younger male users, brother-sister rape is becoming more of a problem. I have personally been involved with counseling a number of these serious family sexual problems. This painful reality is found even in Christian homes.

Families need generic information about HIV as early as possible to prevent unnecessary emotional rifts from forming in what hopefully will become a healing process. In addition, families must be encouraged to forgive any and all "grotesque" behavior for the good of the infected person. AIDS victims will need loving support as much as they will need medical care. Families will need the loving support of pastor, church, and counselor to weather this difficult family problem.

CHAPTER FOUR

AIDS: ADDICTION

Randy

The night air was cool and dry. Uninvited, Randy had followed me from the medical college library where I had been studying across campus to the resident parking lot. My introduction to him had been brief, through another Christian medical student. I had also seen him at the local Christian and Missionary Alliance church.

Outside the library, Randy boldly asked me, "What are you doing tonight?"

"Hi, Randy; I'm on my way home," I answered.

"Do you want to come over to my apartment? I just got some new magazines showing men . . . ," he coyly stated. By then he had worked his hand around my arm.

"Randy, I thought you were a Christian," I said, somewhat surprised.

"I am. But the apostle Paul just didn't understand about us. There are a lot of gays now in born-again churches," he firmly stated.

"Randy, I have no interest. I don't want to look at your magazines," I said as I quickly walked toward my car.

About six years later I was reacquainted with Randy when my partner admitted him to the local hospital. His story may appear contrary to modern theory about the origin of homosexual orientation. It does, however, fit the scriptural definition and portrays a man who was sadly addicted to sex.

His early home life was marred by an absent father and dominated by a militaristic mother. Many people remarked about his effeminate characteristics; but he just passed it off, blaming his mannerisms on the effects of growing up with three older sisters. His social life around high school was normal, except for one aspect: he always said he "dated friends." No serious relationships began in that phase of his life.

When he entered college, he was recruited into homosexuality. At first he was annoyed that he was asked to "participate" in group self-stimulation. The others kept telling him he was born a homosexual, and that he couldn't cover up his true feelings. After a few short months, Randy felt comfortable moving into an apartment with his new friends. He still maintained some distance, but they kept pushing him to join in all the activities.

There was never any question in his mind that Christianity and homosexuality didn't mix. Randy, who thought he had become a Christian about age twelve, believed God had made him somewhat overweight and effeminate for a reason. His friends in college saw no contradictions in being gay and born again. If a roommate had a problem he would half jokingly ask Randy to pray about it. When a minister came to talk to the students about gay rights, Randy suspected that the man was homosexual. In private conversation this suspicion was confirmed when the man told him, "I'm gay because God made me that way. Why not be proud of it?"

Randy and Lawrence, one of his roommates, soon formed a special relationship that was more of a friendship when they were at school, and highly sexual when they were together in the apartment. Lawrence introduced him to the orgasm-enhancing drugs that eventually led to Randy's health problems. After graduation, Randy went to medical school, and his friends left for jobs and further schooling in California.

In medical school Randy was unable to find any kindred spirits. There were no gay churches in the area and he was only able to find two homosexual friends near where he lived. They were not interested in the "sexual habits" of a college-bred, drug-using "hunk." Pornography and self-stimulation constituted their sexual release. Randy had to travel about forty miles to the next university town to find a gay group he enjoyed. A few of the men in this group were into "punishment," and also put a lot of pressure on Randy to supply their medicinal desires and needs. Medical school was the source for the newer medications Randy experimented with. He had stolen a few bottles of IV medications for himself and for the group to inject and enjoy.

The use of drugs, the need for more sex—and more violent sex—and his desire to be closer to the "real world" forced Randy to quit medical school and enter graduate school near his new group. He started smoking crack, injecting tranquilizers or speed as needed, and still was using other drugs for sexual enhancement. He soon had to drop out of school to work full-time to support his habits. This life style was interrupted twice for drug treatment, but continued to escalate until it ended with Randy's admission for AIDS almost five years after he left medical school.

We had a good chance to talk when he was admitted. Anger and bitterness toward his drug habit, toward his mother, and toward people with "straight" attitudes filled our initial discussion. I waited until he was finished and then asked one simple question: "Do you believe that Jesus Christ is your Savior?"

Instead of answering, he mentioned "some other idiot" who had "jerked him around." After I asked him twice more, he finally said simply and quietly, "not any more."

"Did you ever?" I asked.

"I joined the church and thought I knew all about Jesus," he blurted out.

Miraculously, God used our discussion, a pastoral visit, and a renewed friendship to help him see his spiritual need: "real" conversion. Within days Randy's understanding of his past life changed dramatically. Listen to some of the insights that were given to him, not by a Christian friend, but by God's spirit revealing his wisdom.

"I can see now that homosexuality was just as much an addiction as the drugs I was using. Once I was recruited into the fold, I began to crave the high I got from pornography and orgasm. When that wasn't enough I added drugs to make the "high" higher. By the end of college, if I didn't masturbate or have sex five or six times a day, I didn't feel well.

"My addiction to gay sex cost me my medical schooling. My addiction to drugs cost me graduate school. Now, both have cost me my life.

"I no longer desire the beautiful male body. But like any addict, I still desire the high. I will always have the cravings. With God's help I can still be used of him before I'm heaven bound."

HOMOSEXUAL ADDICTION

Randy is not the only person who has become addicted to the homosexual life style. His low self-esteem, his effeminate behaviors, his poor self-image, his lack of a male role model in the home, and his strong affiliation needs opened the door to homosexual activity and experimentation.[1] These were the predisposing factors for Randy's addiction, similar to those of others who fall into alcohol, drug, or heterosexual addiction.[2] The fact that he was recruited and convinced that he "was born gay," demonstrates how recruitment operates as an avenue into the gay life style.[3]

Homosexuality is not a genetic aberrancy; nor is it caused by a hormonal deficiency in adolescence or adulthood. The predominant theory of origin for homosexual orientation is the behavioral model. A certain psychological trauma or lack of development occurs in the early years when sexual identity is being developed. Also, specific abnormal parenting patterns sometimes are found in the homosexual person's home.[4] The prerequisites include abnormal psychosexual maturation, coupled with either a desire to enter or a recruitment into same-sex relationships during adolescence or adult life. For a thorough discussion of origins and counseling of homosexuals, please refer to *Counseling and Homosexuality,* book 15 in the Resources for Christian Counseling series.[5]

No conclusive evidence exists to prove that homosexuality is inborn. However, those of us who have read homosexual newspapers or have listened to the rhetoric of gay activists are aware of some damaging statements regarding their "born-homosexual" ideas. This published information demonstrates recurring themes about recruiting susceptible men into homosexuality.

For example, a widely read gay poet wrote what might be construed as the deepest desires of homosexual men, and possibly the entire homosexual movement, when he penned:

> We shall sodomize your sons, emblems of your feeble masculinity, of your shallow dreams and vulgar lies. We shall seduce them in your schools, in your dormitories, in your gymnasiums, in your locker rooms, in your sports arenas, in your seminaries, in your youth groups, in your movie theater bathrooms . . . wherever men are together . . . Our only gods are handsome young men . . . We will demonstrate that homosexuality and intelligence and imagination are inextricably linked, and that homosexuality is a requirement for true nobility, true beauty in a man. . . .[6]

Not all homosexual men are this filled with hate or espouse these revolutionary schemes. However, the core of homosexual ideology runs deep with themes of recruitment and persuasion throughout the gay activist media. And these are the ideas that filter down the gay communication channels to fill the minds of fence-sitters, new recruits, and homosexual men who need continued motivation.

The other fact that proves Randy was not "born gay" was revealed after his conversion, when homosexual desires and lust for men disappeared and a normal desire for a heterosexual relationship returned.[7] There is much debate about whether homosexual men can develop normal heterosexual desires. But I have discussed this issue with two other ex-gay men who also lost their desire for homosexuality when they accepted Christ. If they were born gay, how could they lose their God-created desires? Both Scripture and gay literature show us that this recruitment, initiation, and subsequent brainwashing are part of the philosophy and strategy of the mainstream "Gay Rights Movement."

The primary aim of homosexual group behavior is the promotion of their sexual philosophy, along with the recruitment of psychologically susceptible individuals.[8] The group shows more militant tendencies than do members of the group individually. Most of my personal dealings with homosexual men and the experiences of some of my colleagues suggest that passivity and gentleness are the predominant personality characteristic of individual homosexual males. Yet the strength of the recruitment message is a sign of the severity of homosexual addiction: Addicts needing more addicts to increase their sexual experiences and enhance their sexual gratification.

Once we understand the depth of this homosexual addiction we can comprehend how the epidemic of AIDS has spread so broadly throughout the homosexual community. A recent study of homosexual males in San Francisco showed that 49.3 percent are HIV positive—one out of every two.[9] This has happened because some homosexual males may have up to five hundred episodes of sexual intercourse with persons with whom they have no long-term relationship.[10]

The addict who attends a bathhouse may have five or more episodes of homosexual intercourse with anonymous partners. A gay man will proposition others to have sex with him by demonstrating the type of sexual activity he wants as others "shop" for their favorite style. Some use drugs such as "poppers" or amyl nitrite to increase the "orgasmic high" reached from these anonymous sexual encounters. Sexually transmitted diseases run rampant in this environment; but the men who contract them often don't care as long as they can still enjoy their sex. Here's how one man expressed this attitude:

. . . I feel like it doesn't matter if I die early because by the time I am thirty I'm dead anyway. I won't be attractive to the people that matter to me. . . .[11]

This fatalistic view of personal worth only in terms of giving or receiving sexual thrills underlies the mind-set of those addicted to their internal "high" created by intercourse.

The classic description of physical dependency or addiction is as follows:

> An individual exhibits addictive behavior when more of the substance or activity is needed to produce the same level of pleasure when compared to previous levels of usage. Often judgment becomes impaired both during use and between use of the substance or activity. Strong substance- or activity-seeking behavior is seen, often causing the individual to seek clandestine or illegal ways to continue their habit.[12]

Homosexual addiction fulfills this definition. Gay men often escalate their numbers of sexual contacts to fulfill their need for sexual release. They attempt to increase the thrill associated with these episodes by using different techniques, positions, or drugs.[13] As discussed above, they are often oblivious to the risks associated with casual sex, which also may lead to involvement with illegal drug usage, prostitution, or violent sexual expressions.

To help these individuals, our counseling must include both the present emotional problems caused by the homosexual activities as well as the behavioral origin of the same-sex orientation. Our efforts will be greatly hindered if we too strongly pursue their reorientation before we deal with their emotional problems. Yet treating the sexual problems as an addiction will foster a better counseling relationship and offer better help to the victims. It will also allow our enslaved patients to diffuse some of their guilt onto their circumstances and environment, making recovery of self-esteem more likely. Consideration of an inpatient treatment program for sexual addiction is wise so that the addiction can be treated aggressively as the ingrained emotional problem it is.

The addiction to a homosexual life style has spread AIDS from Patient Zero to more than three million persons, predominantly homosexual men, IV drug users, and heterosexual persons. Who is to blame for the spread of AIDS in our society? Are homosexuals to blame for their addiction? Do we blame Patient Zero or others who may have delivered HIV to our doorstep? Do we blame the parents of homosexual men for the psychological problems that led to the homosexual orientation? Can we blame sinners for their sin? Who can be blamed?

Each individual must bear personal responsibility before God for his or her individual sin, and as a people we must bear collective responsibility for the sin of our nation. Blaming doesn't rid us of the sin. Only through a proper understanding of the spiritual problems, and the behavioral and psychological problems can we reverse this trend toward sexual addiction that is feeding the fires of the AIDS epidemic. Only when we realize the depth of homosexual and heterosexual addictions can we treat them as the life-threatening habits they are. Drug rehabilitation and alcohol treatment centers can be found from New York to California. But are there fewer sex addiction centers?

HETEROSEXUAL ADDICTION

What about heterosexuals? Can they become addicted to heterosexual activity? Do they show similar signs of sexual addiction, compared with their homosexual counterparts? Is there any literature to support the idea of heterosexual addiction? Is our society exhibiting aspects of sexual addiction? Can heterosexual addiction and promiscuity spread AIDS?

No doubt exists in the minds of those of us who have daily contact with patients that heterosexual addiction does exist.[14] It is most appropriately entitled hypersexuality by those in sexual therapy. Considering the problem with sexually transmitted diseases, teen pregnancy, a 50 percent divorce rate, abortion, and AIDS, it is surprising to see so little media attention to this significant root of the problem. Only a few scholarly individuals have attempted to study this issue in depth, and only a few individuals recognize it as an addiction that must be treated.[15] Most secular counselors are trained just as I was trained, to see the need for sexual gratification as normal, no matter what level of need is exhibited. In nonjudgmental sexual therapy we were taught that bestiality and violent sexuality were acceptable variants of the normal sexual response.[16]

The increasing need for heterosexual gratification often follows a predictable and progressive course. The majority of those following this course are males who cut their sexual teeth on pornography. They start with soft porn and work up to hardcore materials. Soft pornography starts with partially clad to completely nude female models. The pictures and text progress to foreplay, intercourse, and rape. Disease and protection from pregnancy are seldom discussed because they are said to reduce sexual pleasure. The progression to hard-core materials continues from rape, incest, violence, bondage, kidnapping, and homosexual- or heterosexual-group sex with bondage and violence, all the way to child sex, maiming, and murder after rape.[17] The materials and witnesses that were presented to the President's Commission on Pornography demonstrated the depth of addiction that exists into these perverse and grotesque aspects of pornography production, prostitution, and violent sex crimes. This report, along with other studies, strongly suggests that addiction to pornography is a large factor in the commission of rape, sexual assault, and some murders.[18]

The addiction grows as the individual moves from softer forms of sexual promiscuity, adultery, use of prostitutes, and use of legal pornography to the more severe and addictive hard-core forms described above. Those with hypersexual symptoms comprise between 5 and 10 percent of all males. Adding this figure to the 12 percent of men who claim homosexual affiliation, and the silent, unknown quantity of sexual crossover called bisexuality, brings a huge 17 to 30 percent of American males who are mildly to severely addicted to sex or pornography. This group will likely spread AIDS throughout the heterosexual community for the next twenty to thirty years.

INTRAVENOUS DRUG ADDICTION

The role of intravenous drug addiction in the spread of AIDS is now a well-known and well-documented phenomenon. The HIV particle is efficiently passed through contaminated, reused needles and the behaviors that accompany serious drug addictions.[19] Sharing of needles between addicts continues to be an integral and economical part of obtaining and shooting these illegal drugs. Often sexual intercourse and other sexual behaviors are intertwined within episodes of drug use or within their personal or communal relationships.

Addiction to heroin, cocaine, speed, amphetamines, hallucinogens, and IV forms of prescription drugs create severe physical and psychological dependency upon these drugs. The deeper the dependency the more difficult the cycle of drug usage is to break. The intoxication, the lack of judgment, and the drug-seeking behaviors make gainful employment difficult. Fear of hospitalization and loss of freedom to inject drugs keep addicts within their own conclave of fellow users and away from medical professionals who are able to help them. The emotional devastation of the addicted person, the depression and suicidal thoughts, the emotional liability, the greatly reduced self-esteem, the guilt and anger, all cause the addict to desire more drugs—or death.[20] The hope that AIDS would be a deterrent to continued drug addiction doesn't make sense: Some drug users even desire AIDS as an acceptable way to die and rid themselves of the painfully sweet addiction.

With any form of serious addictive behavior, an inpatient, hospital-based program should be sought for the victim. Counselors should be available to help families cope with the discovery of addiction, with the family problems leading to or resulting from the addiction, and with long-term supportive counseling of recovering addicts who will always crave their "junk."

OTHER SEXUAL ADDICTIONS

With the spread of AIDS into the heterosexual community, the epidemic may infiltrate more isolated areas of sexual addiction: pedophiles and violent sexual criminals.

The case of Ted Bundy, one of the most vicious serial rapists and murderers in recent history, brings to light the use of violent pornography as a stimulant for sexual crimes. We must understand that the progression of sexual addiction that eventually induces violent, sexual behavior begins with the gratification of desires with pornography. This often leads to further sexual desires which can only be fulfilled by more "exciting" forms of sexual expression, such as use of prostitutes and illicit heterosexual and homosexual affairs.

As the addiction worsens, the legal and illegal forms of sexual gratification are no longer enough. Violent sexual expressions during intercourse may lead to committing rape. If the addict has been infected with HIV through prior sexual episodes, a chance exists that the rape victim will become infected as well. Only a small percentage of sexual addicts ever commit a violent crime. Yet as the rate of violent sex crimes associated with pornography usage and sexual addiction increases, so too will the number of rape victims who have become infected with HIV.

Sadly, another sexual addiction has to do with children. The desire to touch, take pictures of, and have sex with undressed children is called pedophilia. Many pedophiles were sexually abused children, themselves, some by their own parents and others by known pedophiles. Young children are enticed, bribed, and hooked into exposing themselves for money, toys, candy, or by the threat of violence.[21] Some of the more celebrated cases of known child molestation in recent years have been in day-care centers where parents leave their children in supposedly trustworthy hands. Pedophiles often take pictures of their victims and then may sell them to other pedophiles or share or trade picture collections.[22] AIDS could be transmitted from pedophile to child if rape or sodomy occurs.

The psychological scenario of these sick minds goes much deeper than sexual addiction, alone. Emotional trauma, abuse, neglect, severely dysfunctional families, or a total lack of any family structure leads to self-deprecating and anti-social behaviors that are virtually untreatable through usual psychiatric therapies; spiritual conversion along with long-term psychological therapy has the greatest chance of helping the individual reform. The addictive desire, however, may still remain deep seated in the "flesh" of the pedophile or sexual addict. Helping the addict stay clear of any tempting influences is our best hope of stopping the addiction and possible spread of AIDS to innocent children.

How do we begin to treat these severe forms of sexual addiction? Our role will be limited to helping the patient realize the seriousness of his or her problems from a legal and psychological standpoint. We should be able to direct them to the social

agencies within the community that deal specifically with rehabilitation for sexual criminals. Counseling the family of the victims of a sexual addict also takes care and expertise that may be
beyond our limits. But always remember that we can offer our
support for the addicts who must be incarcerated, offering
encouragement as they proceed through the legal process, and
affirming their spiritual regeneration as they acknowledge
their need for a changed life.

ADDICTIVE SEXUALITY IN THE CHURCH

Is the church any purer than the world? With recent media
exposures of serious sexual addictions among church leaders,
highly visible television evangelists, and well-known Christian
personalities, secularists offer serious doubt about the sincerity
and saving "power" of the gospel. One television evangelist was
addicted to pornography and live modeling. Another lost his
ministry over prostitution, homosexual acts, and cover-up. Still
another evangelist was convicted and is serving time for kidnapping, for having homosexual intercourse with minors, and for
child prostitution.

Pastors have been forced to resign because of pornographic
addiction that led to adulterous affairs or use of prostitutes. One
traveling evangelist spent hours each night peering into win-
dows looking for undressed women or adults engaged in sex.
A deacon has been caught in bed with the pastor's wife. Convicted sex criminals have been known to teach Sunday school,
drive church buses, and lead scout groups.

At a recent National Religious Broadcasters convention, a
well-known church leader relayed this discouraging information about a convention of evangelical pastors and their families:

One of the employees at a major hotel in Washington,
D.C., who was in charge of billing for in-room movies,
was shocked to find that the rooms occupied by pastors
and families at a national convention of these religious
leaders viewed more R- and X-rated films than any other
group—more than physicians, lawyers, accountants, sales-
men, etc.

71

Maybe the other groups had already seen these pornographic movies and didn't want to see them again. Yet the unspoken charge of moral perversion within the lives of these pastors or family members incriminates and greatly damages the testimony of the entire body of Christ.

My own voluntary and anonymous studies of Christian youth, along with similar studies by Josh McDowell and others also related some surprising results, including the estimate that more than 60 percent of all Christian young people had been sexually active prior to marriage.[23] Other studies show as high as 80 percent may have had intercourse prior to marriage. Secular studies show 50 percent of women and 80 percent of men have intercourse before marriage. Does this mean that Christian young people are just as promiscuous as those who do not proclaim a relationship with Christ?

The church is blemished. Our testimony has been tarnished. The world's sexuality seemingly has an open door into the minds and hearts of our youth, and even our church leaders. These statistics alone give us grounds for great fear of AIDS entering and spreading through our own pews and classrooms. Our entire society seems to be hopelessly craving the very sexual promiscuity that will drive the AIDS epidemic into the next century. And almost no one in the evangelical community is honestly dealing with the depth of this serious problem in Christian leaders or their followers.

Why have so many leaders fallen? Why is sexual addiction to pornography and videos, illicit sexual relationships, premarital sexual experimentation, homosexual acts, and even rape at Christian colleges becoming more and more common? Where are we failing to reach our young people?

As counselors, our job description needs to be broadened to include "seminar speaker, health educator, and moral church leader." A dear friend and dean at a Christian university started teaching a class on "biblical sexuality and morality." The interest in building holy, God-honoring male-female relationships was astounding even to him. The class has moved three times into larger and larger classrooms. One of the hottest speakers on Christian campuses is Josh McDowell, who exhorts purity and family communication. *Plague in Our Midst,* a Christian book for lay persons about sexuality and **AIDS**, is being used in "Christian marriage and family" classes, ethics classes, and even as a pattern for a public school sex education programs.[24]

A return to purity within the church will take a painful purging and repentance in those involved with immoral behavior and sexual addiction. Widespread revival may be needed to give power to the newfound sexual purity. The fear of **AIDS** may represent the greatest force in turning people to a spiritual solution to this immense social problem.

Whatever it takes, we must all pray and work within our congregations to make people aware of the sexual experimentation and addiction that is present, and to educate adults and youth about the heterosexual dangers of **AIDS**. Only through a serious effort at repentance and regeneration will we be able to slow the tide of sexual promiscuity and **AIDS** within the church, let alone the rest of society.

CHAPTER FIVE

AIDS: ETHICS

Jackie

It was finally too much! They couldn't take any more. A strange, numb sensation came over Jackie's tired body as she looked over her family's home, smoldering in ruins. The numbness turned to nausea as she ran to a nearby drainage ditch and vomited.

Jackie's family had taken a great deal of public and personal abuse since she had tried to enroll her two hemophiliac sons in the public elementary school. The boys had contracted AIDS through lifesaving injections of Factor VIII, which had unknowingly been infected with the HIV virus. Jackie was poor and divorced, with no money for private schools or tutors. No possibility of home schooling could be entertained because she worked ten to twelve hours a day just to pay the bills. She was confident that no other child in the school was at risk for contracting AIDS from her sons because her physician and all the literature agreed. No casual contact has ever been proven as the cause for an individual's infection, and the risks of a cut or bite were so small that school officials were willing to take that small risk.

The other parents didn't agree, however; nor were they willing to listen to reason, be persuaded by medical experts, or swayed by articles showing little or no risk of spread. They just didn't want their children in the same classes or on the same playground with these "AIDS kids." Their arguments consisted of the usual myths: the possibility of spreading the disease by insects, by a bite from one of Jackie's boys, by a toilet seat, and the additional possibility of the boys' spreading a host of other diseases to their children. They feared psychiatric problems would cause bizarre and dangerous behavior as the disease got worse.

"No one knows for sure, so why should we expose our children to this risk?" the parents asked.

After they had heard from medical experts, the school board and the principal both agreed that the boys should be enrolled, noting that there was no reason why they could not attend school as long as they were healthy and free from complicating infections. So the boys entered school—and the trouble started.

At first, Jackie received a few threatening phone calls. Then an anonymous death treat awoke her from sleep. The boys were ostracized and rejected at school. Each day they would come home crying from the emotional rejection and verbal abuse they received. Some of the school children taunted them by calling them "homos," "gays," and "druggies" along with other profane combinations. They never understood why such meanness was hurled at them. But they somehow suffered through almost two months of this abuse until the ultimate warning was given: Their house was burned while they were eating at a nearby fast-food restaurant.

Jackie and her two boys moved to another town that welcomed them. The family was given a home within a neighborhood that was extremely supportive. The boys were admitted to the local public school and were well accepted by the other children. Not everyone in their new environment knows that these boys have AIDS. But almost everyone who does know loves them and has gone out of the way to help them.

The only difference in these two communities appears to be their residents' willingness to be educated about AIDS, its risks, and its consequences.

ETHICAL QUESTIONS AND AIDS

Other AIDS victims have suffered from discrimination as well.

A forty-five-year-old maintenance worker was relieved of his duties when his employer found out that he was HIV positive. Gall bladder surgery and blood transfusions had been the source of this man's AIDS. As cuts and lacerations were common among the maintenance staff, there was fear of spreading the disease through bleeding or blood-stained tools.

Another family was denied housing because a hemophiliac son was known to be infected with HIV. Life insurance companies now require blood testing before a policy is written, so many people have been denied life insurance because they unknowingly harbor the deadly virus.

Physicians may refuse to treat HIV-positive patients because they want to minimize their risk of contracting AIDS and also because they have patients who do not want their physicians to possibly spread AIDS to them.[1]

Though public hospitals cannot reject patients on the basis of whether they have insurance or not, many AIDS patients could be denied admission to private hospitals when they are unable to get health insurance.

Thousands of cases of harassment, discrimination, violent acts, and slanderous verbal abuse toward presumed victims of AIDS have been documented.[2]

Who has the right to protect themselves, their family, and their livelihood? Who has the right to medical care, psychological care, hospitalization, insurance, or home care? Is it right to fear what is not known and then inflict those behaviors on others because of fear?

The ethical considerations concerning patients with **AIDS** and those who treat them are difficult questions without simple answers. Counselors must appraise all sides of these ethical issues and come to some conclusions based on the best and most up-to-date information available. Our answers will be of help to some, but will be incomplete and unable to answer these other issues. How does the ethical treatment of **HIV** affect the patient, the health-care provider, the family, and society in general? Let's examine the areas of **AIDS** ethics and how they will affect us.

DISCRIMINATION: THE EVIDENCE OF FEAR

The fact that humans discriminate against other humans goes back to the beginnings of recorded history. Even Scripture differentiated between those born to Adam's race, the sons of God, and the sons of men (Gen. 6:1–2.) Study of patterns of discrimination suggest that preservation of groups or tribes and the preservation of the uniqueness of a culture have been the prime reasons for excluding those who were different. Another reason is that people have an inborn fear of those who are different from themselves, especially fearing those who desire to control them. The fear of cultural subversion, loss of a cultural identity, and the literal fear of being destroyed dominated the minds of those who were discriminating and excluding others. Even now, fear, whether reasonable or unreasonable, remains the key factor in virtually all cases of unnecessary discrimination.

The absence of laws meant discrimination, control of a small group over the many, and exclusion of those who didn't "look right." When laws offered adequate protection for groups and individuals, then the fears were diminished and more societal mixing and interaction was seen.

This same emotional engine, fear, is the basis for virtually all discrimination against **AIDS** patients.

People in our society fear **AIDS** for many different reasons. Most do not realize that HIV is virtually impossible to spread except by sexual intercourse or by blood transfusions, also defined as intimate contact. (See Figure 5–1 for definitions of casual, close, and intimate contact.) They erroneously believe that casual contact is possible through such routes as mosquitoes,

77

**Casual, Close, and Intimate Contact
Comparison of Levels and Risk of HIV**

Level	Definition	Risk
Casual Contact	Minimal personal contact, or contact with an inanimate object. (i.e., shaking a hand, touching a doorhandle, using public toilet facilities, communion cup, child in classroom).	No provable risk
Close Contact	Caring for another person, feeding, changing clothing or diaper, caring for minor cuts and scrapes (i.e., caring for an infant, child, sick adult).	Small theoretical risk
Intimate Contact	Exposure to sexual secretions, sexual intercourse, oral sex, homosexual activities, blood transfusions, needle sticks, breast milk.	Provable High risk (Probabilities range from 1 out of 200 for a needle stick to 1 out of 1 for sexual intercourse.)

Figure 5-1

human bites, excrement, kisses, shared tableware, and toilet seats. Because the virus takes so long before it causes discomfort or symptoms, it is impossible to prove whether or not these are possible means of infection.

Therefore, until these routes are conclusively proven to disseminate the disease, we should put aside our fears, reassuring both ourselves and our patients not to be emotionally consumed by these irrational and unrealistic hazards. If we do not offer this information and reassurance, then we will foster discrimination through our inaction.

Meanwhile, information does exist that should provide great comfort. Since we do not have a "casual contact" epidemic of hepatitis B, which is a viral illness identical to AIDS in that it is spread by blood products and intercourse, we can be enthusiastically reassured that AIDS would not be spread by casual contact.[3] Also, studies of those who have lived with AIDS victims, parents of hemophiliacs, and families of homosexual men have shown that living with and around the victims, defined as close contact, doesn't spread AIDS, either.[4] The literature contains a paltry three cases—out of the hundreds of thousands of documented HIV cases—where casual contact is the presumed but unproven route of spread.[5] On the other hand, it is well known that the present epidemic *is* efficiently spread by sexual contact and shared needles among infected drug users, and these routes should be our main focus of attention.

Despite these facts, most non-medical discrimination occurs because of this unreasonable fear of spread through casual contact. Employers don't want to be sued by employees who believe they may get AIDS by working with an HIV infected co-worker. Landlords want to rent their properties without worrying about cleaning the apartment after an AIDS patient has lived there. Also, the fears of tenants living around AIDS patients has been used as justification for housing discrimination.

A larger issue that falls under the label of discrimination, but in reality is more economically based, is the AIDS insurance crisis. In the free market of insurance, rates are based on risk. Those who have very risky health behaviors, such as skydiving, or health problems, such as diabetes mellitus, may not be able to obtain insurance or must pay exorbitant fees for that coverage. It has always been this way.

Because AIDS presents such a high risk, it has been used as a means of insurance exclusion, or noninsurability. Only mandatory situations where insurance is guaranteed to all employees equally gives adequate protection for insurance companies to cover the costs of those with HIV. Otherwise, companies see excluding HIV patients as a wise, legal, and proper business decision. Hopefully, plans which diffuse the costs with higher premiums within large groups will become more available. Meanwhile, the social costs of noninsurability with use of government funds to support AIDS programs or pay for hospital care only increases the cost to each of us as individuals simply because the government is not as efficient as standard insurers.

Discrimination against people with HIV concerning jobs, housing, and schooling is unnecessary except when the health of the HIV patient is at stake, or in the rare situation when an HIV-infected health-care professional could infect his or her patients. Unnecessary discrimination should be halted by reducing fears through education. Legislators should allow some

Provable Risk of Contracting HIV

Situations where discrimination may be appropriate (non-criminal) and necessary (criminal)

Criminal Discrimination

1. Proven HIV-positive sex offender who threatens or accomplishes sexual intercourse with other victims or willing persons without disclosing his HIV status. Incarceration should result.

2. HIV-positive prostitutes who continue to work. Incarceration should be considered.

Non-criminal Discrimination

1. HIV-infected child with a serious illness that is spread by respiratory route such as tuberculosis, CMV, Epstein-Barr, or respiratory syncytial virus.

Figure 5–2

discrimination under the law in rare circumstances where risk is real and provable. (See Figure 5–2.)

MEDICAL CARE: RIGHT OR PRIVILEGE

Americans consider health care an inalienable right.[6] This same attitude of getting better at any cost has created a health-care and economic crisis in the United States. We are spending 11 percent of our gross national product on health care, compared with the 4 to 6 percent spent for health care in other developed nations.[7] Our affluence, our wealth, our standard of living are reflected in this highly technological, but extremely expensive, care for our sick and dying. Yet health care at any cost has never been a right, nor is it protected under our present laws.

Public hospitals have always provided care whether the person could afford it or not. The patients' insurance will be charged or else they will pay "out of pocket." If the patient defaults, then taxpayers foot the bill through the Medicaid program or through direct local, state, or federal tax supplements to these hospitals. Patients with insurance will be charged a higher fee per day of hospital care because others cannot pay. Whether they pay higher insurance premiums or pay higher taxes, those with income will pay for those who don't have income, insurance, or a way of paying a hospital bill.

But will this ethic of "health care at any cost" bankrupt our country, as some suggest? If a large part of the population, from 5 to 20 percent, were to become sick with HIV, it is possible that the payments through our present systems would create an economic crisis of huge proportion. Productivity would plummet because many would be unable to work. Costs for insurance would become astronomical. New hospitals would have to be built to treat these masses of dying patients. The government would spend most of its tax revenues keeping medical care flowing to those in need.

Or will this ethic change?

We are already seeing a number of natural responses to these difficult problems. Many patients are asking through living wills to not have their bodily functions prolonged unnecessarily when the time of death is near. They are also asking that their death occur at home with family, in familiar surroundings. These two responses will greatly lower the cost of medical care if they become the actions of the majority, because dying in the hospital produces huge health-care bills.

Hospice care and other forms of supportive home care for the dying are becoming widely accepted forms of medical care for AIDS patients and their families.[8] Unnecessary medical procedures and hospitalization are held to a minimum and comfort for the patient becomes the primary goal of treatment. Insurance companies and government groups are promoting this type of terminal care through payment incentives for patients who receive care in their home as a means of keeping costs down.

REFUSING TO TREAT?

Can a physician or dentist refuse to see AIDS patients? Is this ethical?

Even the AMA code of ethics supports the physician's right to see whomever he or she would like to see, within reason.[9] But the association has recently stated that it is unethical to refuse to see AIDS patients. This obvious schizoid response underlines the difficulties encountered.

This is a fact: Surgeons cut themselves when performing surgery on patients.[10] Precautions are taken not to spread infection from doctor to patient, but the surgeon is not completely protected from the blood of the patient, in some cases a known carrier of HIV. Shouldn't surgeons be given the option of completely protecting themselves until they can be assured that they will not become infected from a normal part of their job? Once gloves or other procedures can reliably protect from disease, then no rational reason exists for refusing to perform surgery on an HIV patient.

How about dentists? AIDS can be spread to dentists by blood-splattering or by a needle-stick while performing dental work or surgery.[11] To ensure that other patients will not contract AIDS through contaminated equipment, many dentists are going to great expense to clean and replace very expensive equipment. Until the dentist can be assured of protection, and until he or she can assure patients that they are 100 percent protected, wouldn't it be understandable for him or her to refuse to work on AIDS patients?

These two groups, surgeons and dentists, have very real fears for themselves and their patients as they are exposed to blood products many times during an average work day. The suggested "universal precautions" are listed in Figure 5–3 to show the reader what lengths these health-care professions must go to protect themselves, and their patients, from infections with AIDS or other diseases.

What really are the risks for a physician or dentist? How can that risk be assessed? How can it be reduced?

An orthopedic surgeon in New York City would have much greater risk than a family physician in a small town in Virginia, because 25 percent of all cases in the United States are in New York City. Thus the chances of this surgeon performing an orthopedic procedure on an HIV patient in New York is high. Wouldn't it be more correct for surgeons, rather than family physicians, to completely protect themselves by refusing to treat an HIV patient? I don't know any surgeon who would risk a one-in-two chance of contracting AIDS through a surgery. Not many would risk a one-in-a-hundred chance. A few would risk one in a thousand, the estimated risk of a surgeon in New York City. All persons must decide for themselves when a risk is presented whether to continue with their duties or to refuse. We must each decide how much risk is too much.

Universal Precautions for Health Care Workers

Definition: Because medical histories cannot reliably identify all HIV-positive persons, these "universal" precautions are suggested for health-care workers to use with all patients.

Health-Care Workers

1. Gloves should be worn when health-care workers are in contact with blood or body fluids, mucous membranes, or damaged skin. Gloves should be changed after contact with each patient. Masks and face shields should be worn when blood or body fluids are likely to be splattered, along with gowns and/or aprons.
2. Hands and other skin surfaces should be washed immediately after contact with blood or body fluids, or after gloves are removed.
3. Precautions should be taken to prevent injury from needles, scalpels, and other sharp instruments.
4. Mouthpieces should be used if possible for emergency resuscitation.
5. Health-care workers who have damaged skin should refrain from direct patient contact until the condition heals.

Dental-Care Workers

1. Dental workers should use gloves for all oral procedures, and wear protective eyeware and face shields during dental procedures where splashing of blood or saliva is likely.
2. Equipment should be sterilized with a germicide that would destroy the HIV particle after each patient use.

Reference: "Recommendation for Prevention of HIV transmission in Health-Care Settings," 36, U.S. Department of Health and Human Services, MMWR (1987): 5s–8s.

Figure 5–3

Risk can be assessed with our present knowledge about AIDS. It is reasonable and necessary for health-care workers to take all precautions possible to protect themselves from AIDS. The AMA is wrong in saying that all physicians should treat AIDS patients, even without adequate protection. The physicians, dentists, or health-care professionals must make personal, intelligent assessments of those risks and decide for themselves whether to treat or not to treat. Perceived risk should not be based in speculation, fear, and lack of information.

COUNSELING AIDS PATIENTS

The answer to the question, "Is it safe to counsel an AIDS patient?" is a resounding "yes!" Counseling poses no serious risk for the counselors or the AIDS counselees. Shaking hands, supportive hands-on gestures, talking with them, praying with them, even hugging them are all safe behaviors. Besides unethical sexual behavior, a counselor will not contract AIDS from an HIV patient. If the counselors are sick, however, they should refrain from close contact, shaking hands or sitting within six to eight feet of the counselee. The same is true for the AIDS patients if they are sick so that they will not spread a respiratory illness to the counselors. Mutual respect for each other's health should be a part of any professional relationship.

Fortunately, counseling is probably the safest of the health-care professions; it also represents one of the greatest needs for most AIDS patients.

CHRISTIAN ETHICS AND AIDS

It is a sad shame that fear of HIV patients has crept into the church, stealthily undermining the potential we have to minister to this large and growing group of needy individuals. Just imagine if you were HIV positive and you heard some say, "I don't think that I will ever take communion again, because I don't want to catch AIDS from the cup." Or, "My kids are spending the summer at home because I don't want them infected with AIDS at the local swimming pool." Maybe you haven't yet heard these comments, but I have.

When an HIV-infected person hears such paranoid conversations it is no wonder why he or she retreats. Like all sensitive and caring persons, he or she will not want to make others uncomfortable, and will inevitably withdraw from the fellowship.

Because the driving forces behind the epidemic are homosexuality, drug abuse, and promiscuous behavior—behaviors that are "abominations to God"—Christians sometimes seem reluctant to offer a helping and loving hand. One can almost imagine the scene of both the Christian and the HIV patient running from each other. How sad and unnecessary.

There is no one right or wrong view within evangelical circles about how to deal with this issue. Do we let HIV-infected persons attend church? Can they work in the Sunday school? Should they eat at church suppers on reusable dinnerware and utensils? Should HIV-infected babies be allowed in the nursery? Would other church members leave the church, even after they were educated about AIDS, if we allow these situations? Should AIDS patients be allowed to play in the gym where they could be cut and injured? Can we ask people to work in the nursery when they don't want to be around AIDS children? On and on the questions go.

The ministry of Jesus Christ is our best example of how we should minister to others who are infected with contagious diseases and those who are not. His proclamation to his disciples did not discriminate against any physical disease or emotional ailment when he said, "Therefore go and make disciples of all nations, baptizing them in the name of the Father and of the Son and the Holy Ghost . . ." (Matt. 28:19). However, he did tell his disciples to discriminate against those who reject the gospel by "shake the dust off your feet" (Mark 6:11). The only reason for discrimination was for repeated spiritual rejection of God's message of salvation.

Christ, himself, ministered to many persons with various diseases, some infectious, others not. He did not shrink from ministering to those with leprosy, the most feared disease of the day; on a number of occasions described in the New Testament, he laid his hands on lepers to heal them. Scripture is also very clear about our responsibility to minister, as well. We are told that each person, no matter if he or she is an adulterer, a murderer, a thief, a homosexual, or a sexual addict, is equally entitled to God's great gift of forgiveness, just as we are. There are no subgroups, no peoples, no races, no sexes or any other division, including HIV, that excludes a person from this wonderful and free gift.

As believers, we must deliver the message even if it means personal risk to ourselves (such as a missionary ministering to unfriendly tribes in South America who loses his or her life for the ministry). Fortunately, knowledge of God's Word— even a little knowledge—prepares us for whatever ministry he calls us to.

A wise Christian man once told me that "you are safer in any situation within God's will, than you are outside of God's will." Our heavenly Father protects those who serve him. I cannot begin to count the multitude of stories where God gave protection to the believers who were committed to the ministry and to serving him. Similarly, God protects those of us who have been called by his spirit to minister healing and caring to AIDS patients.

However, not everyone is called to minister to AIDS patients, just as not everyone is called to preach the gospel or to administer the programs of the church. Teachers, healers, and mercy showers are gifts of the Spirit God uses to minister prevention to our church members, and healing to those who are infected. The educational areas include preventative lessons about protection from AIDS, including avoidance of sexual promiscuity and IV drug use, and a clear presentation of the scriptural principles involved. Those of us in the healing professions—counselors, physicians, nurses, social workers, and technologists—treat those AIDS patients directly, ministering to their physical, emotional, and even spiritual needs. Showing mercy to AIDS patients with gifts, food, cards, help, medication, and prayers is an area where most people can get involved through giving of their substance or time.

WHY MINISTER TO AIDS PATIENTS?

Should you become involved in ministering to AIDS patients? Should your church open its doors to those who are HIV positive? Should your church set up educational and mercy ministries to those in need?

The church is missing a golden opportunity to minister to millions of spiritually open individuals if we do not open our doors, our hearts, and our resources to this need, both at home and around the world. We will be turning our backs on the estimated three million Americans, and over ten million victims worldwide, if we do not intelligently and caringly construct methods for meeting their needs. Once they are aware that they have contracted a fatal disease, these persons will be open to the gospel, as are all who know their time is limited. This window of opportunity must not be closed due to fear, bigotry, or discriminatory emotions.

As mentioned earlier, I became involved when I was assigned an HIV patient named Leon through our emergency room call roster. The Lord helped me to put aside my natural fears and to see Leon as a spiritually destitute soul who needed my witness of the gospel. As I began to look at the entire picture, my heart was opened to the broad areas of need: for education to youth and parents, for caring ministry to victims, for tough ministry to the sexually addicted, and for an immense spiritual ministry to those dying from HIV.

My travels have taken me to Africa to personally observe the epidemic in the Third World. Later I visited Manhattan Bible Church in the heart of New York City and observed the devastation of the drug epidemic and its contribution to AIDS worldwide. I have met, talked with, and ministered to many of the AIDS victims you have and will read about in these pages. This work has led me to recognize that we have the opportunity for a tremendous ministry to those whose hearts are open.

Sometimes the witness of others, such as Mother Teresa, can call us to action. The examples of other churches and individuals who are ministering selflessly to HIV victims and families is an inspiration we can also use. The Christian Code of Ethics (Figure 5–4) can help each of us to see the whys, whos, and hows of ministering to others, AIDS victims or not. It also underlines our responsibilities within our ministry.

Christian Ethics
Ministry to AIDS Patients

Code of Ethics:
1. Our first and utmost concern should be the spiritual health of others, placing our physical and emotional needs behind the spiritual needs of others.
2. Our responsibility to minister to our families and to other patients may become hindered, however, if we foolishly and recklessly practice our profession and refuse proper education about disease protection and universal precautions.
3. Just as Christ cared for patients without charge, we should be willing to offer some of our professional services in exchange for the opportunity to share the gospel.
4. We must not hesitate to identify unhealthy and sin-filled practices when asked and when appropriate, always remembering our own humble, equally sin-filled state, and that Christ loves the sinner while hating the sin.
5. As the gospel doesn't discriminate against races, sexes, disease, politics, economics, and social conditions, so in our ministering to others we must attempt to treat all persons with equal respect and Christian love.

Figure 5–4

AIDS is a serious epidemic that presents serious problems and tremendous challenges to our society and to our churches. We cannot let the liberal media sweep the epidemic under the rug, ignoring the real causes, and the solutions that must be faced. Our high calling to minister to the sick and suffering of this world must include AIDS patients. To minister effectively to individual patients and their families in our society, we must keep informed of the latest changes and statistics, be willing to ask questions of experts in the field, and know where our resources are when we need guidance and direction.

Though our work through the church must be broad and will be discussed more in chapter 11, the next part of this book will focus on meeting individual psychological and spiritual needs of AIDS patients. This is where we can have the greatest effect on the course of this epidemic: ministering one-on-one to those at risk for AIDS, to HIV-positive persons, to those who are sick and dying of AIDS, and to the families of those victims.

PART TWO

COUNSELING AIDS PATIENTS

CHAPTER SIX

COUNSELING THOSE WHO
NEED TESTING

The epidemic of HIV in our society casts a great cloud of concern over the minds of millions of Americans. A disease that silently is passed among our sexually active members frustrates those who desire the "pleasurable fruits" of promiscuous activity. All of a sudden, they have reason to fear the consequences of their licentious desires.

Who is safe? Which partner will infect them? It seems so unfair to some that the sexually promiscuous of previous generations could enjoy the sinful fruits of "good sex," while this generation cannot do so without risk of contracting a fatal disease. Today, even a one-night stand might lead to AIDS. A society that is so filled with the desire for pleasure, materialism, leisure, and still more pleasure refuses to understand its need for responsibility, constraint, control, morals, and more responsibility. It's no wonder confusion about the epidemic predominates, and belligerence toward those in authority is growing. Anger is aimed at people who speak against promiscuity and how society should deal with it. AIDS restricts personal freedom, subdues pleasure with fear, and calls for discipline of desires.

As counselors, we will see this belligerence when we deal with young persons who are filled with denial, some homosexuals,[1] drug users, and young heterosexual patients, all expressing their anger and confusion toward this "inconvenient disease."

Christian principles provide answers for the problems these young people raise; they serve as catalysts that turn promiscuous behavior into repentance and truly "safe" behaviors. These very principles judge the sin-laden act, but accept and love the sin-laden person.

We can proclaim these firm yet loving Christian principles to our clients, including practical information about when, where, and why to obtain testing for HIV. Our young clients will challenge us to endure their anger, break down their denial, and soothe their confused minds before they will ever consider being tested. And if we cannot break through this hardened emotional shell, these patients will suffer and others may lose their lives. If we do achieve our goal, we must then be able to educate the patients about HIV so we can continue to build our counseling relationship. Furthermore, these patients will need tremendous psychological and family support if their tests are positive.

Each of us has shameful skeletons in our closets, past behaviors that are unpleasant to think about or to deal with. When these behaviors are in the sexual realm of our counselees, emotional turmoil churns constantly until the patients choose to seek testing or counsel. Let me share the lives and circumstances from some patients to give you insight into their emotional pain and confusion.

Robert

Navy life has not changed in centuries. When I was in Africa, I heard reports that American navy men were denied shore leave because AIDS was rampant among the prostitutes of

Mombasa, their port of call. Just as the sailors in the apostle Paul's day wanted to find a port that was "commodious to winter in" (Acts 27:12, KJV), these modern sailors demanded from their superiors to be restationed in another, less risky seaport where they could be allowed shore leave.

These kinds of macho behaviors were just an expected and normal part of Robert's tour of duty in the navy. He served from 1983 to 1987 and traveled mostly through the Pacific basin. When he came to my office, he seemed tired and upset.

"When you were talking about AIDS last night in the marriage and family class, some of the things you said really kicked me in the conscience, and I wanted to know what I should do," Robert said. His story seemed typical for many young men I have met.

While he was in the navy, Robert had had between twelve and fifteen sexual encounters with dates he picked up at local bars or with prostitutes when the "pickings were slim." Once he became infected with gonorrhea and was treated. About half the time he had used condoms.

The last year of his tour, Robert gave his life to Christ through a long discussion he had with the chaplain. He immediately changed his sexual and drinking behavior and made plans to attend a Christian college on a scholarship. Robert's witness to his navy buddies was initially spurned, but later his closest friend also accepted Christ.

On campus, three years passed for Robert with few serious relationships. But then he started dating Renée, a beautiful and talented young lady who had been raised in a Christian home. They both felt strongly about keeping their relationship pure and agreed that they would refrain from a sexual relationship until they were married, if that was God's will for them. But Robert's past kept gnawing at him. He knew that they needed to discuss their prior sexual experiences to some extent; yet he just didn't know how much or what to say. Now that he realized that AIDS could be complicating the picture, he wanted to know what he should do.

"Knowing whether you are HIV positive is a totally separate issue," I suggested during our conversation. "The other issue is one of trust and honesty."

"But I have no idea how she is going to react to my prior sexual contacts and relationships. When Josh McDowell was here, he stressed the chain-of-contact idea: 'You have sex with one person and also everyone they have had sex with as well,'" Robert said.

"Still, your first and most important task is to be tested for HIV. Chances are excellent that you will not have the virus in your system so that you can assure yourself and Renée that whatever you did will not affect her or your children. If you are positive, you need medical treatment, and you need to be fair to her," I advised.

"I just couldn't bear to lose her," Robert said softly.

"What would happen if she found out later, after you were married? What if she was made aware of your previous sex life by hearing the news that your baby tested positive for AIDS? How could she trust you to be honest with her after hiding such an important secret from her?" I asked.

"But I have had friends who lost their fiancées after they divulged their sexual past," Robert said.

"You don't have to tell all the juicy secrets, the how's, the who's, etc. But you should be honest enough to tell her that it has happened, and happened more than once. Then you can add the fact that you are AIDS negative and that you are not bringing any disease into your relationship. Testing you now should cover any sexual relationships that you had during your navy experiences," I said.

Robert took my advice and was tested. As we had hoped, he was negative. He then had a frank discussion with Renée and found out that she had also been sexually active. At first he was devastated. But after another discussion, and Renée's agreement to be tested for HIV, Robert was able to put aside his disappointment because he believed that God did not make any mistakes. They were equally matched by him; their experiences were similar. Forgiveness was traded and their relationship survived the often fatal storm of premarital promiscuity. Their trust and love grew because it was based on honesty and trust.

Ellen

As I walked into the exam room, I could see her depressed expression and the tears beginning to well up in her eyes.

"I've been raped!" she exclaimed as she broke down into tears.

"The movie that was on the other night, the movie about date rape, made me want to get some help. I called the rape companion line, and they suggested that I see my physician," Ellen said.

"When did this happen?" I asked.

"About three weeks ago I went out with one of the guys at work. He knew that I was engaged, and he also knew that my fiancé was in Miami. I didn't want to be alone, and I didn't mind that he held me. But all of a sudden, he become uncontrollable. The rest was like a nightmare. He not only raped me, but I think he gave me some disease. I just feel so dirty," she stated as she again broke down.

The news continued to get worse. Not only had the unprotected intercourse occurred in her mid-cycle, but she was also more than a week late for her period. At the time of her exam, she tested positive for both chlamydia and herpes, two venereal infections. The initial pregnancy test was negative and treatment was started for the infections. She then went home for Christmas break to spend the holidays with her fiancé and his family.

For many people Christmas is the most depressing time of the year. It definitely was for Ellen. Her period never came. The herpetic infection returned with a vengeance one week after the medication was stopped. She repeated a home pregnancy test that was now definitely positive. The physician who tested her suggested that she should have an abortion because of the "emotional trauma" of the rape, the herpetic infection, and the need for longer treatment for the venereal infections. All these stressors led Ellen to cancel her engagement until she was able to deal with each new tentacle of this ever-broadening personal crisis. The only positive news she heard was that an initial AIDS test was negative.

The emotional devastation in Ellen's life led predictably to an acute, reactive depression. She had little regard for herself, for her baby, or for her future. It was in this emotionally low state that she was easily persuaded to consider abortion. A close friend suggested that she see a private gynecologist in a nearby city so that secrecy could be assured. She agreed and later the same week they were seen in a richly decorated private clinic. The initial consultation included repeating some of the blood work and an HIV titer. The abortion was scheduled for the next week. Ellen was quite relieved that her decision had been made so she could begin to put her life back together.

The five days between appointments passed quickly. She had experienced a numb sensation through that week and she showed almost no emotion as she entered the office for her abortion. The physician quietly slipped into the room and sat on his rolling stool. "I'm afraid I have very disturbing news. Your HIV test was positive. I know that you don't want your child to suffer, so I believe your best option is to still have the abortion. You will need treatment as soon as possible for the disease to help slow the progress of AIDS," he calmly stated.

"Does that mean that I will get AIDS sometime in the future?" Ellen asked.

"Unless a cure is devised, or better treatment is found, HIV positivity means AIDS in the future," he stated. Ellen had already rehearsed in her mind what would happen if she contracted AIDS from her assailant. Her family would be supportive, but all indications suggested that her fiancé would not be. If she was going to become ill with or die from AIDS, who would share with her? Who could she care for? Who would be there for her?

She started to cry, then told the physician, "I want to keep my baby! He's the only one who will stick with me through this AIDS thing."

"I think you are making a big mistake," the physician answered.

His words fell on deaf ears as she quickly left the exam room crying. Ellen's friend scolded her and pleaded with her to reconsider until Ellen told her "I have AIDS, and I am going to need someone to cry with me." Her friend was silent the entire way home and never said another word about abortion.

Ellen's emotional trials were rewarded with a healthy, HIV-negative baby boy who was delivered by caesarean-section. She did not breast feed her new son, so that the child would not be exposed to more of the virus. She was seen by the local infectious disease specialist and was started on AZT. Although her life was dramatically changed by the rape and pregnancy, she was afforded the joy of watching her son grow, watching him respond lovingly to her, and occasionally crying with her during those lonely nights.

Pat

Ten years is a long time to know someone like a husband—and yet not know much about him.

As far as Pat knew, her husband Peter was just a hard-working executive who often took business trips to service the company accounts. He worked on the side with a small consulting business and was very open with his wife about the money this generated. He had a separate post office box and would check every few days for mail. Pat trusted him, even if he had become more emotionally distant during the past few years.

The first sign of problems occurred when Pat developed a painful vaginal and uterine infection. She went to her family physician who treated it with an oral antibiotic, and it cleared quickly. When it recurred about two months later, the physician asked Pat, "Did you husband ever have any symptoms?" She was concerned enough to ask what kind of infection it was and if it could be passed venereally. He told her the infection was chlamydia, an infection which could be passed venereally; but Pat never talked with her husband about the infection.

A few months later, she found two "hard-core" pornographic magazines in the garbage can. When she asked Peter if he knew anything about them, he quipped, "I found them by the sidewalk and thought they should be thrown away before some children found them." His response sounded sincere, so Pat didn't ask for any further information.

Within a few days, Pat developed some painful sores inside her vagina. After a positive diagnosis of herpes, she confronted her husband about each infection that she had, and questioned him about his sexual activity outside of the home.

"Sorry, they must be your diseases," he said with an air of sarcasm. "I don't have any symptoms at all."

Three days later, Pat found a note on the kitchen table after Peter left on another business trip. The contents of the note caused Pat to cry so hard she passed out in the living room. He was explicit in his description of the past three years of increasing pornography usage, occasional heterosexual affairs with clients, and his increasing desire for homosexual intercourse and friendships. He stated he would not return and that his lawyer would be contacting her for a divorce.

Fearing the worst, Pat went back to her physician and asked to be fully tested for any and all venereal diseases. After a thorough discussion of the note and her husband's other sexual contacts, the physician counseled her about the testing and suggested she be tested for HIV. She consented, went through with the exams and the blood work, and then went to talk with her pastor. She didn't have anyone else she could trust with such disturbing revelations about her husband's bisexual life style. He offered her help and became the support that she needed.

Wisely, the pastor offered to go with Pat to hear the test results. He even spent some time before rehearsing some of the possible outcomes, problems, and future plans. This preparation was badly needed—the HIV testing, along with the herpes test, was positive.

Brian

"Doctor? I'm afraid I may have AIDS. I would like to be tested," this baby-faced, red-haired young man told me after he had heard me speak in a church near Boston.

His story was similar to Robert's. After high school he had signed up for air force training. While he was in the service, peer-pressure and cajoling led him to the usual alcoholic and sexual releases. Then two friends introduced him to the "joys" of "all-male sex." He never enjoyed anal sex, but continued to participate until soon after he was restationed, when he ceased all homosexual activity.

Within six months of discharge from the service, Brian was already serious about a girl he met at school—Kim. They had similar interests in music and athletics, both were somewhat reserved, and both had red hair. The usual "weekend home to meet Mom and Dad" was arranged so that if all went well, the engagement would be announced at the end of the visit. Each was happily anticipating making it formal.

But one evening Brian's fiancée asked about his previous sexual experiences, quickly stating that she was still a virgin. He seemed lost for words. His response was jumbled and uneasy, trying to skirt the issue. Instead of lying to her openly, he suggested that he would be a compatible partner.

"I've already set up an appointment to see the doctor to make sure that all the plumbing works correctly," he jokingly said, attempting to lighten the heavy air of mistrust that was building. "I think you ought to have an exam, too, because we have to think about birth control. I don't think the Lord would want us to have children the first year or two until we are able to afford them."

She agreed and the subject was dropped.

When Brian spoke with me later, he said, "I need to know how to tell her of my previous mistakes without destroying our relationship"

"You do need to be honest with her, that you have been sexually active. Let her know that you made a mistake, that you were sexually active, and that you have taken all the blood tests and precautions to make sure that you are disease free," I suggested.

His exam and HIV titer were negative; no problems were found. Brian then shared his negative exam and negative HIV test results with his bride-to-be. But she didn't handle it well. She started to ask him about previous homosexual contacts, which he reluctantly but honestly admitted. She then scolded him severely for not sharing this earlier in their relationship.

"Whatever love I had for you dried up with the revelations of your inner perverted sexual tendencies," she yelled. "I never want to see you or talk with you again!"

Attempts from Brian to communicate and ask forgiveness were rejected over and over again. One evening, after Brian and his roommates were in bed, Kim's mother called.

"Brian, I am sorry that Kimberly cannot forgive you for your prior sex life. My son is also a homosexual. The pain that has brought our family, especially Kimberly, has been overwhelming. He's being treated for AIDS in Philadelphia right this minute. I'm sorry that we couldn't tell you this before, and I know you will understand why Kimberly feels so strongly."

Jennifer

The images of her exotic past breezed through Jennifer's re-laxed mind. She remembered the beauty of the Rift Valley with its reddish hues of the clouds framing the early evening sun as she had watched it from the escarpment. The memory of the awesome power and size of a thundercloud that the pilot had to fly around on the journey from the northern Turkanan tribes caused her to give praise to the awesome God who created such beauty. In her memory the images of the tall, dark, beautiful, yet shy, Massai tribes people, who are said to be some of the fiercest warriors on the face of the earth, were as clear as a photograph. The warmth of the tropical rain forests, the climate of paradise, the sudden and soothing afternoon rains, the sear-ing heat of the deserts even in winter all filled her thoughts while she traveled home to the United States—possibly never to return as a missionary.

Her traveling companion was God's greatest gift. As she had ministered in the northern section of Kenya, another mission-ary, David, had come to work with the tribal peoples, sharing his specialty of linguistics. As David and Jennifer had worked together, they discovered some startling similarities about each other. They had been born in the same South Carolinian county, and for a short time, had gone to the same school. After their spiritual conversions, they had both felt the Holy Spirit drawing them to eastern Africa. Uganda had been the initial target; but both had been delayed by the political rav-ages of the Idi Amin era of murder and carnage. Then they had both been stationed in Jinja, near the Nile River bridge where thousands of decayed bodies had been discovered by a British hydroelectric engineer. Both had committed their lives to the spiritual and physical needs of their African brothers and sisters.

Jennifer's health, however, had begun to fail. The intermit-tent fevers, swollen lymph nodes, weight loss, and abdominal pain sounded so familiar to her African physicians. They had often seen this pattern of symptoms and called it "slim disease," the African term for AIDS. However, it seemed to come and go too quickly for slim disease, so the physicians suggested she see her American doctors for another opinion. She knew if the diagnosis was positive for AIDS that her mission board would not send her back to the land and the people she loved. Though she was sad to leave, she was glad that God had allowed her to minister to so many sick and dying patients, to whom she spoke words of spiritual comfort.

For the last two years, Jennifer had worked as a medical assistant, drawing blood, running lab tests, handing out medications, giving injections, and assisting with surgical patients in the operating and recovery rooms. She could remember at least ten different times when a patient's blood had soiled her hands or her clothing, or splattered in her face. With her knowledge of AIDS, she just assumed that she was infected, but trusted Christ to strengthen her to continue her ministry in Africa.

Anxiety was not a problem for her; yet she could not put aside some of her fears. She feared knowing for sure that she had AIDS because that would disqualify her from serving on her chosen mission field. But she loved David so much that she had to know to protect him. He didn't care if she was positive or negative. His love and his decision to marry her would not be affected. In fact, he had already decided not to use protection during intercourse so that they would, as he thought, "bear all burdens together." If she died early, he didn't want to be far behind. He knew that God could protect and prolong their lives if that was his will.

The smile on her face could not have been broader when she emerged from the consultation.

"To God be the glory! I don't have AIDS!" she exclaimed and excitedly hugged David. They jumped, twisted, turned, and ended up embracing on the floor.

"What did the doctor say was the problem?" David asked.

"He found two different parasites and thought that I probably had mononucleosis, or a form of it, as well. He suggested that I rest for six months, take the medications he prescribed, and recheck with him three times before we return to Africa," she said with obvious joy.

"God's provision is always perfect," David shouted. "In his time and in his way, it's always perfect."

To Be Tested or Not?

For every person who believes he or she might have AIDS, there are many logical and rational reasons to be tested, and probably as many not to be tested. These ideas range from fear of taking the test, fear of a positive result, fear of what others will think if they ask for testing, to the more profound fear of discrimination and fear of deadly illness.[2]

The emotional and social complexities of these issues are endless, unless some basic truths are remembered about these patients.[3] People have a better chance of preparing themselves emotionally and spiritually when their HIV status is known and they have been properly instructed. If the test results are negative, their fears are relieved. If they are positive, treatment can be arranged, the patient can prepare emotionally for the illness by completing the grieving process, and they can have an opportunity to seek spiritual guidance, encouragement, and salvation.

The counseling process would be frustrated and short-changed, however, if we simply and directly told all our patients, "You should be tested." True, each person who has even a minimal risk should be encouraged to be tested, but also to continue further behavioral counseling. Otherwise, patients would lose the opportunity to gain insights about their fears, their guilt, their relationships, and their grief, and we would not be able to offer the interactive communication and counsel during their time of hurting and confusion.[4]

For example, Robert's situation represents a common counseling problem for pastors, parents, and health-care professionals, and it offers some interesting thought for discussion. His reasons for refusing to be tested were all speculative: First, he feared losing his relationship. The desire not to be emotionally wounded by his fiancée's sexual promiscuity was also a strong reason for not wanting to confront the inevitable. The guilt and remorse he experienced about his own sexual mistakes would have to be relived if the topic was brought up for full discussion. To discuss previous intimate relationships would break their agreed-upon ban on intimacy in the sexual aspects of their relationship. I'm sure that Robert had a score of other rationales for his reluctance to discuss his previous promiscuity. And that reasoning transferred to his reluctance to be tested.

In contrast, the reasons Robert needed to be tested were all positive and concrete. His risk of contracting AIDS was low and his chance of relieving his fears would be high. If he loved his fiancée, he would not want to risk exposing her to the deadly virus. Knowing his HIV status would help him discuss any future plans they would make as a couple. If, by chance, he was positive, he needed good medical care and treatment for HIV, and time to adjust emotionally to the changes in their relationship.

Emotional fears and speculations usually add confusion to the decision-making process. Rational, concrete, medical, and psychological reasons for knowing the truth should supersede the "emotional don'ts" and persuade the fence-sitting individual to be tested. But the patient is helped by exposing these emotional issues. It also provides a golden opportunity for counseling that we should not abridge.

Like Robert, Ellen had a host of what seemed like good, emotionally based reasons for not knowing whether she was HIV positive. After the disintegration of her engagement, the only persons she had to protect were herself and her unborn child. In the depths of her depression she had been willing to sacrifice the child so that she could rebuild her relationship. But a positive HIV titer meant her fiancé would not take her back. This left Ellen and her unborn child to weather the storm together.

Wisely, the medical community has seen the protective medical rationale for testing pregnant women such as Ellen, for testing men and women who contract other sexually transmitted diseases, and for testing those (with patient consent) who are at risk and require surgery or transfusions. Ellen's decision to refuse testing would have to be made prior to seeking medical attention. It also might exclude her from obtaining prenatal care for herself and her child. Though the decision to test is wise, HIV does represent a psychological barrier to health care for many poor, pregnant women who feel the test could be used against them.

But the concrete reasons for knowing are helpful in making both short-term and long-range plans. After she knew she was

HIV positive, Ellen more fully realized the humanity of her child and stopped the abortion. Then she was able to progress from fearful unknowns to difficult circumstances where she was able to work through her grief and losses while finding proper support.

Ellen's story represents the nightmarish side of AIDS, the one-in-a-million chance of contracting HIV from a transfusion or a forced sexual contact. But she could not move on emotionally, seeking the support or medical care that she needed, unless she was tested. Knowing her HIV status clarified her choices, allowed her to stand by her convictions, and rallied her family to her side.

In Pat's story, the hidden issue of her husband's bisexuality opened other insights into the testing issue. The trust that Pat had in her husband was commendable and remained unchallenged due to his skill in hiding his extramarital sexual encounters. Why should Pat have questioned her husband's fidelity when she contracted a simple infection? She really had no reason to be tested until several facts became clear enough to warrant concern. Then she did made the right choice to be tested quickly while seeking appropriate emotional support.

Once we know the painful outcome of Pat's story, we might be tempted to suggest HIV testing for all our patients when they suspect their spouse has been sexually unfaithful. However, testing is not appropriate for all persons and should not be suggested until emotional speculation has turned into solid fact.

WHO SHOULD BE TESTED?

I see many people in my office who are concerned about whether they should be tested. Suspected but unproven marital infidelity, sexual contacts before 1980, casual contact with possible AIDS patients, excessive fears of HIV in the environment, and many other irrational reasons for asking for testing are often given. But we should not recommend expensive medical consultation and HIV testing for those who have no need for concern. If our patient shakes the hand of someone who has been given a blood transfusion, for example, then our patient has no reason to be tested or to be concerned.[5]

Thus, a major weapon in our counseling strategy is to educate our patients about the virus, the manner in which it is spread, and the likelihood of contracting the disease at a certain level of contact. We should always listen to their concerns and acknowledge them as real, our first task. Second, we should educate patients about the virus. Third, if there is any sexual contact, or if there is unrealistic concern that will not be dissuaded with education, or if there is need for absolute confirmation with a negative test, then we should be firm in suggesting the patient have his or her blood tested.[6]

There are other questions to consider. Can we trust the testing? Are there inaccuracies and other problems with the testing about which our patients should be informed? Does a positive or negative test result always mean what it says? When should repeat testing be done?

HIV TESTING

Blood testing for HIV is now very common and inexpensive, less than fifty dollars per test. Testing is never perfect, however, but HIV tests are designed to err on the side of calling a test negative unless it is absolutely, conclusively positive. We err on the side of missing a positive test because the severity of the disease and the stigma attached to a positive test are so foreboding.

For a test to be positive, the patient's blood must contain antibodies, small proteins produced by the immune system, that are specific for and bind to the HIV particle. Some patients who contract the virus will not produce antibodies to the virus for more than twelve months; yet they could still pass the virus by sexual contact or by blood transfusion.[7] The average time between contact and the time an antibody test becomes positive is two months. Fortunately, we are very close to approving direct-antigen testing, which looks for viral particles in the blood. This would mean a positive test could be obtained within a few days after exposure and infection.[8]

Each blood sample is submitted to two screening tests for HIV. If they are both positive, a special electrophoresis procedure, called the Western Blot Test, is performed. This test involves looking for pieces of the HIV particle. If most of the pieces are present, then the test is positive. If a few or none are present, the test is read as negative, even though the two antibody screening tests were positive.

Sufficient antibodies are found in the blood after the first two months to cause the testing to be positive. The tests remain positive for many months to years. But as the disease progresses, the immune system becomes weaker and begins to fail. At this point, a person's antibody testing may again be negative, because the immune system is so feeble that it can barely respond to any infection by producing antibodies against the virus. So the patient may have a negative test but still be filled with the AIDS virus, able to spread the disease, and to continue to reap the destruction it causes to the immune system.[9]

LATENT PERIOD

The characteristic of the HIV particle which causes such emotional difficulty and global spread of the epidemic is the latent period, the extremely long time between infection and the appearance of first symptoms. Jay, for example, contracted the disease in Haiti in 1979, but did not show symptoms until 1987. He died in early 1990, ten years and a few months after he became infected with HIV. Our counselees may be infected and have a positive test, but not have any signs or symptoms. Without concrete evidence of the disease, they will ask, "Why should I be tested?" The risk of spreading the disease to others and the possibility of early treatment become the major reasons for testing.

We may be tempted, but should not use this long latent period as an excuse to suggest testing for everyone. Those who are exposed sexually, those who have had potentially tainted blood transfusions, those who have injected intravenous drugs, those in health care, and those family members who have had intimate or repeated close contact with an AIDS patient should be tested. Those who fear they are infected but do not fall into one of the above groups should be counseled, educated, and not tested unless extreme emotional distress persists. Testing for these patients with emotionally driven mind-sets based in irrational fears is expensive, but can be therapeutic.

In our counseling, the inevitable question will arise: "Is there any chance that I could have AIDS?" We should offer at this point to refer the patient to a knowledgeable physician who will confirm the patient's history, assess the risk of HIV, and offer testing if appropriate. It has been my experience that many physicians will not take the time to talk adequately with the patient about his or her risk, what a negative or a positive test means, or whether the patient should be tested again. Many patients also want to know "if I'm negative, how do I stay that way?" Pastors, counselors, and even trained lay counselors can provide a necessary ministry by filling in these gaps for the millions in our society who will have questions and will need sound advice.

ASSESSING RISK

Who is at risk for contracting AIDS? What are the levels of risk?

A previous patient, Brian, will help us see the benefits of assessing a person's risk while we counsel him or her about the other issues. Brian was engaged in homosexual contacts in 1985 and 1986 with fellow shipmates from small cities in the United States.

A great number of factors are found when assessing a person's risk for HIV. Generally, these can be broken down into three simpler categories; behavior, time, and location.

The activity Brian was involved in was an extremely high-risk behaviors: anal sex.[10] The more episodes of intercourse by this method, the more risk. If these episodes were interspersed with IV drug usage or use of prostitutes or other promiscuous relationships, his risk would have increased. If Brian was addicted to pornography use and self-stimulation (masturbation), that would have decreased his risk. The more risky the behavior, the more episodes of unprotected intercourse with greater numbers of partners, the more risk of contracting AIDS. Brian's behavioral risk was high.

The time that Brian had his homosexual contacts also makes a difference. If he had been sexually active in the 1970s, he would not be a risk. If he had remained active with homosexual intercourse into 1990, his risk would be very high because a large percentage of practicing homosexual men are already infected with AIDS. The higher the number of sexual contacts after 1980, the higher the risk of AIDS. So Brian's time risk was small.

The home town of any sexual contacts, the location where transfusions originated, and the place where any sexual behaviors occurred can also be important. As stated earlier, an estimated 25 percent of all AIDS and HIV cases presently occur in and around New York City. Other cities that have high levels of AIDS include San Francisco, Los Angeles, Dallas, Atlanta, Miami, Washington, D.C., Philadelphia, and Chicago. Smaller numbers of AIDS patients and HIV carriers are found in small cities and rural areas. The closer the behavior occurs to New York City or another large city, the greater the risk of contracting AIDS, because many of the homosexual and IV drug use communities found in our country are located in these large cities. Both of Brian's sexual partners were from smaller cities, reducing his location risk.

Brian participated in a risky behavior, but only twice. The time was early in the epidemic, so the risk would be small. And the contacts were from small cities, where AIDS was practically nonexistent. Thus, Brian's overall risk was low, which was confirmed by his negative test. But he definitely did have some risk and absolutely should have been tested. If he had lived and had multiple homosexual encounters in New York City in 1989 or 1990, then his risk would have been extremely high. Figure 6–1 demonstrates this method of risk assessment and its various gradations.

BENEFITS OF KNOWING

Many persons who practice risky sexual behaviors suggest that the knowledge of a positive test would ruin the rest of their lives. "So why be tested?" they ask. Their greatest fear is easy to see. If they are positive, they would have to stop their promiscuous behavior or become responsible for the pain and death their behavior causes another person.[11] A fear of losing their precious "freedom" to continue in sinful promiscuity is the motivating factor for not being tested.

The loss of beauty, freedom, and sexuality is a real cultural fear among male homosexuals who become "sexually worthless" to their lovers once tainted with HIV. A positive test could

Assessing Risk for AIDS

Behavior: Certain behaviors carry an increased risk for HIV.

1. Homosexual intercourse (oral, anal)	Extremely High Risk
2. Intercourse with an HIV-infected person, male or female	Extremely High Risk
3. Intravenous drug usage (shared needle)	Extremely High Risk
4. Multiple sexual partners	High Risk
5. Intercourse with prostitutes	High Risk
6. Intercourse with use of condom	Moderate Risk
7. Few heterosexual partners	Low Risk
8. Intravenous drug usage	Low Risk
9. Abstinence/marriage	No Risk

Time: As the epidemic increases, certain time frames also confer greater risk.

1. Risky behaviors after 1990	High Risk
2. Risky behaviors from 1985–1990	Moderate Risk
3. Risky behaviors from 1980–1985	Low Risk
4. Blood transfusions from 1980–1985	Low Risk
5. Risky behaviors before 1980 (Europe, Africa, Haiti)	Low Risk
6. Blood transfusions after 1985	Very Low Risk
7. Risky behaviors before 1979 (USA)	No Risk

Location: The epidemic has spread from the homosexual and IV drug communities within the cities to other areas of the country.

1. New York City	Very High Risk
2. Other major U.S. cities (San Francisco, Los Angeles, Chicago, Miami, Atlanta, Dallas, Philadelphia, New Orleans, Washington, D.C.)	High Risk
3. Small cities, rural areas	Low Risk

Figure 6–1

make them "rejectable." And if they are rejected, they might as well be dead. The prodromal psychological factors often include a home filled with rejection, a trauma that many homosexual men can no longer handle. Often, homes filled with rejection, and the resultant fears of further rejection, are strong motivational factors in initiating, pursuing, and continuing promiscuous homosexual relationships.

The fear of knowing one's HIV status is greatly outweighed by the benefits of testing, no matter what the end result is.

Our last example, Jennifer, illustrates the usual outcome and some of the complicating factors. Her fears would have continued to plague her had she not been tested. She was at risk for AIDS and she was aware of that risk by her medical knowledge. The shattered glass, the needle sticks, the blood all were possible carriers of the deadly virus. The number of her patients who were assumed to have had AIDS (not by testing, but by symptoms) had been between 5 and 10 percent. The number of HIV-positive patients to whom she had been exposed could have been as high as 20 to 25 percent. Her status as a missionary was questionable until her health problems could be resolved medically. Even though her fiancé would not have abandoned her if she was positive, he needed to be as protected from the virus as possible.

The risk of infecting others, exposure to the virus, living in a country where AIDS is present, all affected her psychological state, and all needed to be faced. Her spiritual maturity, a loving and supportive fiancé, and a desire to serve her Savior, no matter the cost, kept her grief and anxiety to a minimum.

In the United States, AIDS is a treatable condition. Medications can be used to treat the immune system destruction by the virus as well as the opportunistic infections that occur in the latter stages of AIDS. New studies show that the earlier HIV patients are started on medication to slow the progress of the disease, the longer they will live and the fewer medical complications they will encounter.[12] Beside the benefits of early medical care, early counseling should be available to deal with the family problems, the grief, the sexual questions, and the spiritual problems that result from an AIDS infection. Because most of the patients who are tested will be negative, relief from fear will be the reward of a great majority of our clients.

We must still remember, however, that AIDS is not curable and it is considered a fatal condition. Our hopes must be realistic and cautiously muted.

Most of the HIV-positive patients that I have talked with suggest knowing is better than not knowing, because they are able to "take control" and deal with their medical treatment and with the other problems it creates. The few who have said they were "sorry" they were tested continued to have promiscuous sexual relationships, were often fatalistic about their treatments, and refused to discuss their grief, guilt, or remorse. They were infected and they preferred to be miserable rather than helped. They were also unconcerned about infecting others with a deadly disease. These persons with hardened hearts and eyes blinded with sin present the most serious challenge to curbing this epidemic through education and counseling.

ANTICIPATORY COUNSELING (PRE-TEST COUNSELING)

The pastor who helped Pat after the discovery of her husband's double life used anticipatory counseling to soften the impact of a positive test. It allowed her to deal with the emotional issues related to that discovery. Within medical and professional counseling, we use other names for other types of anticipatory or preventative counseling such as "premarital" counseling and "pre-employment" screening.[13] Counseling our patients before a hospitalization when a serious disorder has been tentatively diagnosed allows the patient to see all emotional sides to the issues of disease and death.[14]

This same anticipatory counseling can be used with persons at risk for HIV. Dealing with their present emotional state, the fears, guilts, anxieties, and relationships helps them sort through these confused reactions to their devastating predicament. We can discuss the personal and psychological ramifications of both a negative test as well as the dreaded positive test. A sample sheet of anticipatory questions is contained in Figure 6–2.

IF THE TEST IS NEGATIVE

When I traveled with a small medical and evangelistic group to Kenya and Uganda in 1988, fears about AIDS were constantly on my mind. Every medical procedure had to be protected. Every exam was accomplished in a way to prevent the spread of blood or secretions. Knowing the latent period of the virus, I couldn't just fly home, be tested, and forget about it. Though the risk was small, I had my blood tested almost twenty months after our trip. Fortunately, it was negative. As you can imagine, I quietly rejoiced for days.

Anticipatory Counseling
Preparing Patients for the Results of HIV Testing

1. How would you feel if your test was negative? How would you feel if it were negative, but the physician told you to be tested again in six months?

2. What would your reaction be to a positive test? Identify your feelings and why you have them. Would a positive test change your life? How? What negative changes would you anticipate? What positive changes can you imagine?

3. Have you made any plans for telling others if your test was positive? How would you tell them? Why would you tell them?

4. How would a positive test change your job, your family, your relationships? Would your relationships be improved or hindered by telling persons you were HIV positive? What do you believe their reaction would be? Do you realize that most people react supportively when told a friend or family member has HIV?

5. Where would you seek medical help? Could you take medication every four hours? How would you feel about a disease that takes a lot of care, of lifestyle changes, of commitment and discipline? Do you have family or friends who could help you keep disciplined about your health?

Figure 6-2

The fears associated with AIDS are real and understandable. Rational people often are given misleading or false information about AIDS that makes them concerned. We need to acknowledge these fears, educate our clients if they are unrealistic, and be very willing to suggest testing if they have been exposed through a risky behavior. These fears can cause serious emotional problems or even physical problems and symptoms. We should not minimize them unless we want to lose them as clients.

Hopefully, most, if not all, of those we counsel will be negative for HIV. What does a negative test mean? As discussed before, it depends on when the risky behavior occurred. If a young man had homosexual intercourse two months ago and he now has a negative test, then we must suggest further testing in four months (six months after exposure), and in ten months (twelve months after exposure). He must also be told not to expose anybody else through sexual contact or through blood donation until all the testing is negative.

If clients have engaged in some potentially hazardous behaviors more than two years prior to having a blood test, then they can be virtually 100 percent sure they do not have HIV when a negative result is returned.

STAYING FREE FROM AIDS

A negative test is just the first step. The second step is to remain HIV negative by abstaining from the risky behaviors that spread the disease.

Often a crisis fear of HIV will bring a patient to counseling. We are then given the opportunity to open our counseling relationship by listening and discovering the emotional needs within the person, his or her family, and his or her relationships. These needs may drive the young person to "act out" against parents by partaking of sexual or drug promiscuity. We must determine whether or not the patient has been promiscuous and what risky behaviors the patient has used.

The next step is to educate and suggest testing if it is appropriate. We can use anticipatory counseling to further assess the psychological needs of the individual and help him or her to approach testing with some assurance of the ability to handle the potential outcomes. Once the test results are known, follow-up must be suggested and further education and support must be given to keep this patient from making the same, risky mistakes again and again.

This is where our real counseling begins.

Abstinence is the surest way to prevent AIDS. However, remaining abstinent from sexual activity and drug usage is very difficult for the immature person who has deep emotional and family problems.[15] Helping our patients to overcome family problems, low self-esteem, and guilt, while exposing the addictive and dependent character qualities that could cause them to make the same mistakes is more important than our prior assessment and diagnostic time. When they are negative, we may have a difficult time keeping them negative if we do not disciple them, counsel them, and nurture them. Our spiritual sights must be high because losing this psychological battle may mean losing our patient as well.

CHAPTER SEVEN

COUNSELING WHEN THE TEST IS POSITIVE

Sandra

"Would you sign this consent to let us test you for AIDS?" the resident physician asked. "We cannot find any reason for you to have yeast growing out of your bowels. We need to check all our options."

"You mean AIDS, that gay disease?" asked Sandra, almost choking on her words.

The resident then sat down with her again and asked her all the same questions about drug usage, sexual activity, transfusions, and exposure to other AIDS patients. And again, Sandra denied them all.

"I'm sorry that I forgot to tell you about a boyfriend I used to have," she said. "We did have intercourse a few times, I think three or four. But that was almost three years ago, and I didn't get pregnant or didn't get clap or nothing. We used a condom a couple of times."

"Was he sexually promiscuous, or did he ever inject himself with drugs?" the young physician asked.

"I did see him with another girl at a bar about six months later. He also offered to buy me some pills if I ever needed them," she said.

After sharing a few more details with the physician, Sandra reluctantly signed the consent form for the AIDS test. She was told that medications were now available to treat AIDS. It was also likely that the bowel infection, if it was caused by HIV, would not get any better until the immune system damage was stopped. The test results would take about three days to come back from the lab.

While waiting for those results, Sandra made some phone calls to see if she could track down her old boyfriend. Mutual friends were called to find out where Jack had gone and what he was doing now. Seven calls later she talked with his sister in Yonkers, who informed her that Jack had died about five months before—from an overdose of heroin. Although his sister did not positively know, she was sure that he committed suicide because he was depressed about this drug habit and a "disease" that he acquired from his habit. Weight loss and chronic cough were the symptoms he complained of most, two common symptoms of AIDS.

The next morning Sandra heard what she and the physician now suspected. She was positive for HIV, and her T-lymphocyte (helper cells) count was below four hundred per cubic millimeter. She was graded as a Stage 5 AIDS patient, in the Walter Reed classification. (See Figure 3–1 in chapter 3.)

A nearby teaching university was continuing to enroll new HIV patients in its AZT study, and Sandra was judged to be eligible for the study. She was immediately transferred to their outpatient clinic where she was treated for the bowel infection as well as AIDS. Initially, she responded to both of the medications and improved her weight, her T-helper cell counts, and her general health.

One weekend a month, I cover for the local family practice residency program, and that's how I met Sandra. It had been seven months since she was accepted into the university AIDS study, and now the diarrhea and infections had returned and were taking their toll. In spite of her weakness, though, she was very willing to talk and share her experience with others.

"I always protected myself from those men who try to steal from the girl," she stated. "I saw my father manipulate my mother and that made me sick. But when Jack came around, I sensed that he really loved me. I had never shared with anyone before. We even waited for a couple of weeks before we had sex; but as soon as we did, then the relationship changed. He acted liked he owned me and tried to get me to do things for him. It was my father all over again. I gave him something precious. He gave me this disease, this horrid thing. I'm glad he killed himself. Otherwise, I would have killed him."

"Will you ever forgive Jack for what he gave to you?" I asked.

"If God will take this AIDS away, then I might consider it!" she said.

She remained resistant to any spiritual discussion, claiming God was just as responsible as Jack. She didn't want to have anything to do with either of them. Sandra remained bitter about many things, including the care that she received.

The diarrhea, the weakness, and the weight loss all continued. Soon she was too weak to feed or care for her daily needs. She remained hospitalized for one month and then was transferred to a nursing home. Thirteen months after her diagnosis with AIDS, Sandra died.

WAITING FOR THE TEST

A positive AIDS test will be as devastating to our patients as finding out they are dying from cancer or some other terminal disease. Many of our patients realize that AIDS is an incurable condition. They have seen the news reports, documentary stories, and tabloid descriptions of people who are afflicted and dying of this disease. Yet a positive diagnosis will affect people differently depending on how they are counseled prior to and following the testing.[1]

Many people are unprepared to cope with a disease where

the first symptoms remain hidden for months or even years. Then, when the test is suggested, extremely personal questions about intimate issues such as sexual orientation, promiscuity, and IV drug usage are fired point blank at the patient, who is already reeling from the emotional impact of a deadly disease. The patient must wait until the test is run twice and confirmed with a Western Blot Test, presenting a delay of three days or more before the result can be obtained.

A series of questions may run through the patient's mind: *What happens if my test is positive? Is AIDS the cause of my other infections or my weight loss? Is AIDS as fatal as everyone says? Are the treatments effective? Is any pain involved? Why won't someone talk with me about AIDS?*

The more thoroughly we educate our patients about HIV, the better they will handle the testing process and the results. Sandra was not prepared. She was unexplainably sick at the time when HIV testing needed to be done. Nor did she have great concern about AIDS, because the media classified it as a disease of drug abusers and homosexual males, and she was neither. She could see no fairness in God's will when others were able to have intercourse hundreds of times and never become infected with any disease. She had had sex only four times, but was still cursed with a fatal venereal disease.

The counseling time we spend before the result has been returned will build the patient's trust and openness with us, hopefully allowing them to share deeper psychological needs. Helping our patients discover their dependency and affiliation needs, some of the psychological needs that promiscuity fulfills, can promote a changed attitude toward these risky behaviors, protecting them and others in the future.

Many times promiscuity represents a self-destructive attitude, preceded and accompanied by abusive parenting, complicated by low self-esteem, and exacerbated by emotional problems such as depression.[2] Often, the more self-destructive the behaviors, the deeper the family and personal emotional problems. The lack of a spiritual commitment or a total forsaking of a previous spiritual commitment adds to the rebellious denial that characterizes those caught in any self-destructive or addictive cycle of behavior.

117

Breaking through this rebellion, and helping our patients see the causes of these self-destructive feelings gives them the ability to forgive themselves before they have to deal separately with the consequences of that behavior. If the cycle is not broken before the testing is done, then a positive AIDS test may drive the person deeper into other self-destructive behaviors and relationships. Many secular psychologists and sociologists see this pitfall of a positive test pushing an already disturbed person deeper into emotional turmoil and self-destructive behaviors. Many refuse to suggest testing for anyone because of the fear of doing more harm than good.

Breaking through a rebellious attitude, offering a caring counseling relationship, educating about HIV, and giving loving support and encouragement should be our counseling goals while we wait with the patients for their test results to be returned.

WHAT DOES A POSITIVE TEST MEAN?

A positive test means that patients have been infected with the virus through one of the behaviors or situations previously discussed. Their bodies now have the virus growing within the immune cells. Patients are capable of passing that virus by sexual contact, by the use of IV drugs, or by a blood donation. Once the test is positive, treatments can be started that may prolong the lives of these patients, possibly until a cure can be found. We have found that keeping AIDS patients healthy, with a regimen of good nutrition, exercise, and disease prevention, also prolongs lives.[3] New treatments to stimulate the failing immune system are now in the experimental stages. Other treatments are being discovered and tested on a regular basis. (See Figure 7–1.)

Although treatments for the physical sequela of HIV and medications to slow the viral destruction are being refined and improved at a rapid rate, little discussion and research is occurring on counseling strategies for HIV patients. Secular psychologists refuse to counsel patients about the dangers of continuing their sexual expressions, suggesting that "safe sex" or use of a condom is adequate to prevent spread. Tacit approval of fulfilling their sexual appetites is granted while the

Treatments for HIV
Medically Approved Medications,
and Medicines Being Tested

Medically Approved Medications

1. AZT (Zidovudine): slows the progression of HIV infection, blocks viral spread
2. DDI (Dideoxyinosine): Slows the progression of HIV infection, blocks viral spread
3. Trimethoprim/Sulfomethoxazole: Treats Pneumocystis carinii pneumonia
4. Pentamadine: Prophylaxis for pneumocystis infection (given by aerosol)
5. Chemotherapy agents: Treatment for Kaposi's sarcoma
6. Antibiotics, antiparasitics, antituberculin medications: Treatment of opportunistic diseases

Medications Being Tested:

1. Analogs of nucleic acids: Similar to AZT and DDI, for the treatment and spread of HIV
2. Vaccines: Being tested to prevent initial introduction and spread of HIV
3. CD4 blockers: Agents that fill the CD4 receptors so the virus cannot penetrate the lympho-cytes or brain cells
4. Interferon: Used to treat tumors by increasing immune system responsiveness

Lifestyle Changes:

1. Avoiding infections: Hand washing, staying away from sick children and adults
2. Eating a highly nutritious diet: Balance with maximal doses of vitamins, minerals, trace elements, and lower in fat and cholesterol
3. Daily exercise: Regular, strenuous but not injury producing exercise
4. Active spiritual exercise: Prayer, meditation, fellowship, study

Figure 7-1

secular psychologists attempt to relieve the patients of their "sexual frustrations and guilt." This vicious cycle cannot be broken until we refine our strategies and aggressively counsel our clients of the seriousness of continued sexual activity.

Our counseling strategies for this decade and beyond must include sexual and illicit-drug abstinence, aggressive inpatient or outpatient treatment for those with severe sexual or drug addictions, intensive family therapy and family involvement in the disease process, and caring ministries to the many who are slowly dying of this dread disease. Individual counseling strategies depend on the needs expressed during assessment and can be integrated into the general counseling framework of dealing with the fear of disease, dealing with the grieving process, and dealing with acceptance, growth, and maturation.

DEALING WITH FEAR

Fear may be the greatest motivating factor ever known. God uses its potential in softening, moving, and molding the hearts of human beings. In his design, the love of the heavenly Father is the most important positive factor he uses to motivate people to follow and obey him. But on the opposite side, fear of pain, death, and hell can also turn a rebellious heart toward its maker (Matt. 10:28).

Thus we must admit that the negative emotional and physical responses that fear evokes can have a positive purpose. Pain protects us from continuing to inflict suffering on ourselves. We remove ourselves from situations or predicaments that cause pain; we shrink from problems we know are painful and unpleasant. Fear of pain can even cause paralysis, preventing us from entering into a bad or dangerous situation.

The protective aspect of fear and pain is designed into our bodies, found in the automatic protective mechanisms within the nervous system. This has been termed the "fight-or-flight" response of the autonomic nervous system.[4] When the body is challenged with a fearful situation, it unconsciously responds by increasing the heart and respiratory rates, moving blood to the muscles from the other organs, etc. A proper physical response to fear is designed to protect the body from pain and death.

When counseling with HIV patients, we should offer specific education to help allay unnecessary fears about the disease while still acknowledging the truly fearful aspects of AIDS: disease, pain, and death. We must teach patients about healthy behavior, allowing the power of this negative motivation to protect both the patients and their potential sexual contacts.

What is that fear telling our patients? Must they change their promiscuous behavior into God-honoring behavior? Are they responsible for their actions before a holy and just God? Is forgiveness available to them from a Savior who was tempted by the fears of pain and death? Hebrews 2:18 offer this answer:

"Because he himself suffered when he was tempted, he is able to help those who are being tempted."

Patients can be shown both sides of fear—the positive aspects which yield spiritual fruit and emotional growth, and the negative side which leads to stress, inner turmoil, and physical discomfort. An example of the positive and negative aspects of fear is found in holocaust victims. If they became emotionally fixated on the fearful aspects of potential death, then they deteriorated both mentally and physically over a short period of time. Those who were able to project a positive future, one filled with hope, were strengthened by their emotional outlook and were able to quell the emotional holocaust within.

Fear can be a great ally in our counseling, opening the heart, bringing to the surface any emotional damage, giving insight to relationship problems, and helping our patient see his or her personal spiritual need.

GRIEF AND ILLNESS

The test for HIV was positive. In the midst of all our education and counseling, the reality of the infection is slowly sinking in. Hearing this news, the minds of our patients will be set ablaze with the profound emotional reactions commonly classified as grief. Most patients who are ill will grieve. Grief represents a healthy but painful reaction, designed and ordained by God for a positive spiritual purpose within his loving will.[5]

All persons who fear death will react emotionally with denial, guilt, anxiety, bargaining, confusion, anger, and sadness— which usually leads eventually to a healthy response of acceptance and growth. These reactions protect our tender emotions from a harsh reality, and they are usually initiated by denial. As the reality of the problem becomes evident, anger and sadness normally give way to bargaining and depression. However, one grieving patient may move smoothly from denial to depression, from anger to acceptance, while others may be bounced back and forth from bargaining to anger to bargaining to bitterness. Healthy grief reactions move steadily toward acceptance, even though a few rough spots and U-turns may need to be accomplished. The persistent cycling of these reactions is termed pathological grief, a crippling but treatable emotional disorder.[6]

Grief will be evident in each stage of AIDS. I remember Jay describing his reaction when he was first told he had the disease. He was so shocked that he could not speak. As the physician left the room, he started crying and said to himself over and over, "How can this be, God?" He cried for hours and clung to the only human who showed any concern, a compassionate nurse whose voice Jay described as "the most comforting I've ever heard."

Our patients may react emotionally during each of their illnesses, during the infections, during the setbacks, during the treatments, and during the remissions. They may begin to grieve long before their deaths, continuing to slide deeper into the emotional abyss of despair. Each infection will remind them of their disease, their mortality, and raise their fears of pain, death, separation, and loneliness.[7] With some guidance and counsel, hopefully each episode will remind them of God's love instead of his anger, of his forgiveness instead of his judgment, and remind them that the disease's purpose is to bring us closer to him, not to separate us from him.

ACCEPTANCE AND GROWTH

Cese, the high school senior described earlier, conquered her grief as well as any I have seen.

"I've accepted the fact that I have AIDS. I know that it seems unfair to others when they know I was raped and forcibly given the disease. But God used the pit and the jail to bring Joseph to the place where God could use him. God can use me more effectively with AIDS than without. I'm just trusting him for the strength and courage if and when he calls me home," she said.

God's purpose for pain, suffering, and grief is to bring us to our knees, to call us to total reliance upon his strength and not our own. Thus, when God calls us to grieve, he also desires for us to accept his purpose and to grow in faith and trust in him. Acceptance is the benchmark, where normal grief matures into acceptance and growth. Otherwise acceptance is snuffed out; this leads to persistent pathological grief and spiritual rebellion against his purpose.

Sympathetically, we can cry with our patients, leading them

gently through the emotional reactions of illness. Soon, however, we must lay before them the goal of grief, helping them to see acceptance as the first step toward emotional recovery and spiritual rehabilitation. Since AIDS often causes continued and persistent deterioration of the body and mind, it may lead to dementia, a weakened ability to function mentally.[8] But emotional and spiritual growth are still possible, even when the eventual paths are divergent—deterioration and death of the body, but maturation and life for the spirit.

HONESTY AND INFORMATION

I can remember at least twenty different cases in which a family member approached me before the diagnosis was finalized, asking "Please don't tell Aunt Betsy her diagnosis. She won't be able to bear the news."

In each situation, I carefully explained to the family that honesty is the most important treatment I give my patients. Without it, they cannot grieve, they cannot plan, they cannot set their affairs in order, and they are cheated of the opportunity to settle their spiritual accounts. It is unethical in a great majority of circumstances to withhold medical information from a competent, mature patient.

Every one of those patients could "handle" the information that was lovingly given to them in simple language they could understand. The tactful offering of facts, the honest exchange of personal information, builds the counseling relationship at the same time it helps the patient. Just as children know when an adult is hiding the truth from them, adults are usually just as able to spot a lie or an evasion of the truth when they are given serious news.

Withholding or purposely hiding information about AIDS when a patient is positive for HIV is unethical and unwarranted. It is just as bad as the multitudes of cases that I have read in which one sexual partner was HIV positive, knew it, knew he or she could pass on the disease, and yet, withheld this lifesaving information from the other sexual partner. Honesty must be the basis for all counseling and professional relationships, as well as all post-testing relationships with an HIV-positive patient.

How Patients Can Protect
Themselves and Others

The number of patients who are HIV positive and who will not exhibit any symptoms will continue to grow as the epidemic spreads. In this early stage of the disease a question that is often asked is "How do I protect myself from infections, and how do I protect my spouse and my family from HIV?" It is a question I have heard again and again from AIDS patients.

Many HIV-positive patients will have normal immune function early in the course of their disease. The number of T-lymphocytes may be diminished, but not to the point where patients will be plagued with infections.[9] Early studies of HIV strongly suggest that contracting other viral or venereal infections potentiate HIV, causing the disease to become very active, accelerating the destruction of the immune system and the destruction of opportunistic infections.[10] An important part of our counsel to patients will be to suggest they cease promiscuous sexual activity for the sake of their own health. Protecting themselves from others who are ill with mononucleosis, CMV, or other serious respiratory viruses is also prudent.

AIDS patients do not have to become hermits, however, hiding from all diseases and the people who carry them. Normal hygiene and extra handwashing will help prevent the spread of colds, flus, viruses, and other infections to the susceptible HIV-positive person. Covering all cuts with an antibiotic ointment and a bandage slows bacterial growth and the potential for serious infection.[11]

Protecting others from HIV is also simple if they are kept from intimate contact, sexual secretions, needles, and sharp implements used by the patient, such as razors. Also, if the HIV patient is sick, he or she may pass a respiratory illness (not AIDS) more easily to others, so some sensible precautions and avoidance would be suggested. Any cuts should be covered with antibiotic ointment and a bandage, whether you are the patient, a family member, or a friend.

Our counseling can be even more helpful if we pass along this simple and practical information to our HIV clients and their families. Figure 7–2 offers you a summary of these practical

Protecting Yourself and Your Family

Guidelines:

HIV is transmitted by sexual intercourse, sharing of needles contaminated with HIV-infected blood, and from mother to child in the womb and through breast milk. Rarely, a transfusion can or could cause infection with HIV. There is no evidence and no proof that HIV can be spread by any of the following methods:

Mosquitoes	Hand-to-hand contact	Biting
Ticks	Communion cup	Kissing
Lice	Sharing tableware	Swimming pools
Toilets/Showers	Telephone/Office equipment	Water fountains

Persons with HIV should be allowed to work, to go to school, to attend church, and to do any and all activities they would like except having illicit sex and sharing IV drugs.

Protecting Your Family

1. Teach children to follow the scriptural principles for sexuality: abstinence from sex until marriage. Build their self-esteem, develop their decision-making abilities, teach them how to say "no" to things that can hurt them physically, emotionally, and spiritually.

2. When your children are mature enough to understand, talk with them openly about sexual experimentation, pornography, the world's philosophy of "sex for pleasure," teaching them to understand that enticement leads to problems (venereal disease, HIV, teen pregnancy, abortion, educational deprivation from premature sexuality). Honestly is one of the qualities children desire most in their parents. Communication is the most important activity you can accomplish with your children.

3. Theoretically, the only way HIV can be passed from one person to another without intercourse is through the exchange of blood products. One way this could occur is from bleeding cut to bleeding cut. Good medical advice to prevent bacterial infections of cuts suggests you cover the cut with an antibiotic ointment, then with a bandage. This would offer protection against the almost-impossible spread of HIV from cut to cut.

Figure 7–2

suggestions that can be reprinted for patients and their family members.

KEEPING FIT

Good health is not only something one is blessed with; it also takes work. Each of us benefits when we eat nutritiously, exercise on a regular basis, reduce our stress, get regular and adequate rest, communicate to improve our family relationships, and grow in faith toward our heavenly Father. Staying fit spiritually, emotionally, and physically becomes an essential discipline for the HIV patient as well, helping to prevent illness and delay disease. This may be the most important aspect of patient protection we can suggest.

Few controlled studies of AIDS patients have been completed that show benefits from these fitness areas, but science has proven the theory of fitness leading to improved health. Other studies have shown the lack of fitness causing and potentiating disease. For instance, studies have proven that negative stressful life events, such as death of spouse, stresses of work, and chronic fatigue decrease the immune function of people with normal immune function.[12] Nutritional studies of people with proper eating habits, compared with others who had nutritionally poor habits, suggest that the immune system can be compromised the longer these bad habits persist. Common sense would suggest that taking care of one's self, staying away from disease and stress, and enjoying solid relationships with family members and God could only benefit the health and longevity of the HIV victim.

We should discuss this "life-style" therapy early in the course of HIV counseling. Holding the patients accountable for healthy dietary changes, physical activities, and communication patterns will mean our counseling can have "medical," good-health benefits.

LIVING, WORKING, AND PLAYING

"I just couldn't let anyone know that I had AIDS. They would have kicked me out of the apartment, and I might have lost my job!" one AIDS patient said to me.

Most of us could not imagine the neighborhood burning our house down because we have curly hair. My employer would never fire me because I caught the "flu." My friends would never refuse to play basketball with me because I was overweight. Yet AIDS victims are often treated with as little sense as is exhibited in these analogies. AIDS is as dangerous to my neighbors as my curly hair. Employers don't fire employees who have a contagious respiratory illnesses. So why should HIV-positive employees be fired if they have a contagious non-respiratory illness? AIDS victims need exercise just as overweight, middle-aged men do, and both are equally dangerous on the basketball court.

No housing restrictions should be placed on an HIV-positive person simply because he or she is not a danger to others in an apartment building, a house, or a condominium. Even living in a communal situation, such as a dormitory, a camping cabin, or a fraternity house presents an extremely small risk to roommates of the AIDS person. The roommates are only at risk if they are promiscuous sexually, use IV drugs, or if the rare situation were to occur that the HIV-infected person would happen to bleed on a roommate who also has an open cut or sore. The opposite is true, however. The risk of catching a serious infection is much greater for the AIDS victim whose immune deficiency turns usually minor ailments into much more serious illnesses. For the safety of the AIDS victims, they should be offered more private and less contagious accommodations.

A few opinions I have read stress the "danger" of allowing an AIDS victim to work alongside of other, healthy employees.[13] They suggest people with HIV carry mononucleosis, CMV, and other illnesses that are contagious by the respiratory route. Other employers stress the possibility of injury and bleeding as potential routes of spreading the disease to other employees. Even food-management services have voiced opposition to serving AIDS employees because of supposed "special" cleaning requirements needed for their utensils. If, in fear, we take these arguments to their logical conclusions, we should ban AIDS victims from driving so they can't be in an accident to bleed on anyone, from working so that they could not cut themselves or cough on someone, or eat in food services and restaurants because of these special cleaning requirements. This line of reasoning is totally illogical and has been proven to be unnecessary.

The proof is rhetorical for those who are willing to listen. Are other similar viral diseases, such as hepatitis B, spread by utensils that are not adequately cleaned? Do fellow employees contract diseases on a regular basis from others at work? Aren't we more likely to die of injuries in a car accident or work accident than we are to contract and die of AIDS?

There is no risk of contracting HIV by taking classes with, handling money from, or talking with a person who has AIDS. Proper education of those administering first aid at the work place would make handling an injured AIDS victim a safe procedure. No special procedures are required for cleaning food utensils, glassware, or dishes to protect others from HIV. There should be no restriction upon any person with HIV as to employment or living situations.

Is it safe to engage in recreational activities with those who are HIV positive?

Some fears were initially raised about inadequately chlorinated swimming pools and the possibility of spreading AIDS. These fears have been shown to be unreasonable and swimming has been shown to be safe.[14]

Fortunately, there are no restrictions for those with HIV as to recreational possibilities. Virtually any sport in which the individual would want to participate presents no added risk of HIV to others. Softball, swimming, scuba diving, tennis, sailboarding, fishing, skiing, and a whole host of other sports are allowed and encouraged for good mental and physical health. The only precautions necessary are simple, and apply to other persons with health problems as well. If the immune system is weakened by diabetes, mononucleosis, or HIV, then those persons should reduce their activities and try to maintain an even temperature inside or out. Also, if an injury occurs, someone should be available to handle the injury properly while protecting himself or herself—and others—from HIV-infected blood.

PREVENTING DISCRIMINATION

It is an unfortunate and sad fact that human beings have always and will always discriminate against someone who is different, who presents rapid change, or who carries an unknown disease or disorder. The information age has broken down the discriminatory barriers held for so many years against those with epilepsy, with mental retardation, and with cancer. Education has been the key factor in helping people to understand these disorders, allowing the unaffected to put aside their fear-filled reactions in favor of caring actions and helping attitudes. This educated enlightenment continues to break down racial, cultural, and even political barriers at a tremendous pace all over the world.

However, some will consistently resist information, education, and even criminal penalties for discriminatory practices, remaining in their bitter attitudes of prejudice and bigotry. In fact, if we are honest with ourselves, most of us have attitudes toward certain sexual, violent, or unhealthy behavior that nauseate and repel us, though we may not react outwardly toward the behavior. Discriminatory feelings are part of normal, social, human behavior. But actions based on those feelings should be suppressed. We should be as tolerant of others who hold some emotional prejudices as we hope others will be tolerant of ours.

AIDS presents some unique problems, some that can be answered through education, others that cannot be answered until future research reveals more complete information. The education of family and friends of those with HIV should stress the safety of daily interactions and caring for basic needs, while underlining the importance of "abstinence" from risky behaviors. (See Figure 6–2 in chapter 6.)

When dealing with resistance among believers, we can evoke the spiritual side of the "discrimination" argument. Christ would not discriminate against group or person—sinners, heathen, adulterers, those of different race or nationality, Romans, Greeks, Scithians, those with leprosy, epilepsy, bleeding disorders, or demon possession. We must follow his example as we are called to spread the gospel to "all creatures." There will be no excuse as we stand before the judgment seat of Christ for our petty and unnecessary patterns of discrimination.

If education and information won't break the attitude, if the spiritual arguments fall on a hardened heart, then possibly the "experiential" factor will melt a discriminatory nature. Seeing the AIDS epidemic in all its horror, seeing the innocent children whose parents reject them, the children whose parents have died, the children who have AIDS and no relatives to take them in, seeing these victims face to face is bound to soften even the most hardened person. Reading about some of the real-life cases that you can find in many journals, magazines, and books, including this one, will put real faces on this real disease.

Ministering to all who are infected with HIV is a huge job, whether they are positive without symptoms, ill with the disease, or in the final stages of life. Each of these patients deserves our open and caring attitudes without any hints of discrimination or fear. They deserve family and friends who are able to support them in their time of need. They deserve a society filled with rational information that does not put these precious, needy, souls aside. They will need our help as their health wanes, as their families become more distraught, and as they become painfully aware of their spiritual needs before their heavenly Father.

CHAPTER EIGHT

COUNSELING THOSE
WHO ARE ILL

Martin

Late in the evening, Martin had completed his two-mile run and then had eaten with friends at a local health-food restaurant. Back at home, he was reading and watching the news when he began to feel warm. For the last few days, he had known that something wasn't right in his chest. Within fifteen minutes, he was shaking violently and began to cough. The sweat soaked his shirt and continued to pour off his forehead.

He called the rescue squad because he knew he couldn't drive in his condition. The paramedics rushed him to the emergency room where he was seen immediately by the physician.

"Get the cooling blanket down from ICU," the doctor

shouted. "And get this man packed in ice—his temp is 107 degrees."

Intravenous fluids were started to prevent shock, and Martin's temperature was quickly lowered to 102 degrees. Amazingly, he did not have seizures or sustain any other neurological damage from his extremely high fever. Though he could not talk when he arrived at the emergency room, the physician had recognized him from previous visits and knew that he was HIV positive. After the cultures were taken, antibiotics were started to help stop the bacterial spread through the blood stream. But the specific type of infection was not known.

Within minutes, Martin became more and more short of breath. Blood gases tests showed his oxygen content was dangerously low. An endotracheal or breathing tube was placed in his lungs to help him breathe. Then he was placed on a ventilator and given medication to calm him and relieve the distress of the mechanical breathing. The oxygen content in his blood improved quickly.

He was transferred to the intensive care unit and watched closely while he was on the ventilator. It was a full three days before his lungs had improved enough for him to be removed from the machine and have the endotracheal tube removed.

Martin had one of the best infectious disease consultants in the state. This physician had seen him on a regular basis until Martin had lost his job five months earlier. After Martin's suspicious layoff at the company, he was unable to find another job, and he remained unemployed. Without a job, he could not buy the medications he needed; so he let his AZT prescription lapse, even though he might have gotten it free through a medication procurement program.

Martin survived several episodes of pneumonia. But with each new episode he became more of a recluse. The crying spells came more often. Panic attacks, set off by the reality of loneliness, also came more often. Trivial problems would set him into an emotional tirade which would often end in crying, cursing, and hitting, reactions similar to a four-year-old's tantrums. About four weeks after he was discharged for the latest case of pneumonia, he showed up in the emergency room again, crying uncontrollably, asking to be admitted to the psychiatric service for help.

Deidra

"So you still aren't taking your medication, are you?" the physician asked.

"I still don't see what you're so concerned about," stated Deidra smugly. "It has not helped my skin; I think you have given me the wrong medication."

"As I have explained before, the AZT is for the disease that is reducing your immune function. These tumors called Kaposi's sarcomas have infiltrated your skin because of your AIDS infection. Don't you understand that taking the AZT is meant to help your AIDS infection, not the Kaposi's sarcomas?" the physician said with some indignation and disgust.

"But that's what I mean. I came to get these yucky brown patches off my skin, and you say I have some other disease that I couldn't possibly have," Deidra said angrily.

The diagnosis of AIDS had been known to her family physician and a host of specialists for about two years—but Deidra had consistently denied it. She had been sexually promiscuous in the San Francisco area during her college years, 1984–1988. But she claimed that all of her partners were "men," and not homosexuals. Ever since her first case of Pneumocystis carinii pneumonia, she persistently had denied that she could have AIDS or HIV or any "gay disease." She did not use IV drugs, she said, and had never had a transfusion, or traveled to Africa or Haiti.

Deidra's denial had been severe, often causing her to ignore important symptoms that were related to her disease. Counseling had been offered to her a number of times. She went once at her mother's insistence but refused to acknowledge any understanding of her disease or even the possibility that it existed. She continued to believe AIDS is a "political and unreal disease," one that "Republicans have used to discredit the gay lobby and gay Democrats," she often said.

"How could I have a political disease?" she would ask the therapist.

No matter what pain, fever, or other symptom arose, Deidra

didn't tell anybody. Usually her mother had to spot some problem, wait until it became extremely obvious, and then force her to see the doctor. Deidra might be chilling and coughing, yet in the doctor's office she would say, "I'm fine. I don't know why I'm here."

Harold

"God's ways are always better than man's ways. I've refused to go to the mission field for so many years, I guess God had to get my attention in a powerful way," Harold said.

People were always the problem for Harold. His church friends were always fighting or gossiping or quarreling, and they never seemed to love each other as the Bible commanded. He was so disappointed by his fellow church members that he could never believe God would call him overseas or to an inner-city church where he would just have to put up with the same un-Christian attitudes.

The skills Harold had developed over the years were perfect for a mission hospital. He was trained as a medical technologist, had a Bible-school background, and had taken some youth evangelism classes to augment the talents he used with youth groups. His occupation, which kept him sheltered from "people problems," was as a laboratory technician, running and analyzing blood, urine, and other specimens. Knowing the danger, he was usually careful; but on a number of occasions he had been splattered with blood and shattered glass. Once he had a partially healed abrasion on his face when he accidentally splattered himself. Supposedly, this was the episode through which he had contracted AIDS.

Harold's AIDS diagnosis was difficult to make. When he became ill with persistent fevers, tiredness, and liver enlargement, doctors at first thought he might have hepatitis, but all the tests were negative. The CMV testing was positive. Yet he remained ill for sixteen months. The initial HIV test showed a positive screening test, but a negative Western Blot Test. The repeat test later, however, was positive.

"I can accept having AIDS. I knew it could happen to me or to anyone. There is no hope for me to turn back the clock and make the decision to go to the mission field. In fact, I am convinced that whether I was in the United States or I was in Africa, ministering where God called me, I still would have contracted AIDS. Now I have years of missed ministry to catch up on and a disease that may not let me catch many of them," Harold said.

THE REACTION TO DISEASE

Imagine yourself in the physician's office. You are there because your stomach has been hurting, you have been unable to eat, and you have been nauseated for almost a week. This scenario is not that atypical; many have been through a similar ordeal.

You might think your pain is due to gall-bladder problems, a stomach ulcer, or maybe colitis. You might dread the thought of surgery for the gall bladder, but you are sophisticated enough to know that medication is probably all that you need.

"I'm sorry to have to tell you this. You have a large malignant tumor of the pancreas that is ready to obstruct a number of vital functions. It is too large to resect at surgery. . . . You have between a few weeks and a few months to live," the physician tells you in a somber but firm voice.

How are you going to react to this terrible news? Would you describe the physical sensations of shock like being swallowed by a pit of quicksand, the smothering sensation of life being squeezed out of you? Could you comprehend the diagnosis, the severity of the prognosis? Is it possible to believe what you just heard?

The news that you are dying would probably be as devastating to your fragile human emotions as the news of the sudden and unexpected death of your spouse or your child. And yet, God created within your remarkable mind a means of protection to soften the brutal blows of emotional pain and suffering. These mental defenses are well described and studied within our modern body of psychological knowledge.[1] They represent methods used by the emotional areas of the brain to accept the reality of suffering without the "news" resulting in a serious psychological separation from that reality. Failure of that system may result in an acute psychotic break; the emotions become unable to handle the reality of the crisis. Failure of these emotional defenses also occurs when the individuals become so mired in the reaction to the disease that they fail to gain any greater understanding of the reality. This blockage or failure to grieve is termed pathologic.

Psychological reactions to pain, disease, suffering, and death are often discussed under the larger heading of grief. The process of grief has been described as a multi-staged task of adjusting psychologically to the reality of loss. Many theories, orders, plans, descriptions, and schemes for the grieving process have been devised by psychologists and psychiatrists who have studied persons involved in crises, illnesses, and death.[2] But all of these jumbled and discordant theories can be reduced to a simple two-staged process that describes the secular view of grieving. These two phases are the reaction phase and the acceptance phase. No matter what order the reactions occur, and no matter which descriptions are used to describe the "emotional process of grief," these emotional reactions originate in the defense mechanisms meant to protect the mind from emotional overload.

Scripture, however, ascribes a special purpose to grieving which necessitates a third stage, the most important stage of grief.

Suffering would be devoid of spiritual purpose if we stopped at the acceptance of the loss, the second stage. I have attempted to underscore this spiritual plan for grief by outlining a three-staged grief process named the "Unified Theory of Grief." It is more fully described in *Counseling the Sick and the Terminally Ill,* book 20 in the Resources for Christian Counseling series.

God intends grief to bring us closer to him, to demonstrate our need for his grace, and to build and mature us into the image of Christ. Pain, loss, suffering, and death are designed by a loving heavenly Father to remind us to place our faith in him, and to retrieve us from sinful influences that daily tempt us.

We react emotionally whenever we are sick, when we lose a family member, or when we become terminally ill. The emotional reactions to each of these situations are similar, but the degree and longevity of the reaction is different depending upon the seriousness of the illness. Your grief reaction would become much more intense if you had been told you are dying from pancreatic cancer than if you had been told you have an ulcer and must give up pizza.

When we evaluate an **AIDS** patient, we will usually have to deal with more intense and severe emotional reactions. Once the patient knows the disease is fatal nearly 100 percent of the time, he or she will probably have a more intensive period of grieving.

What are some of the common emotional or grief reactions of **AIDS** patients?

Denial is the most common defense reaction in any illness. Deidra could not accept the diagnosis of **AIDS** cognitively or emotionally. She had always understood it as a disease of homosexual men, the most common mode of spread in the Bay Area where she attended college. But she also had some other previously untold emotional reasons to persist in her denial. When she was seven years old, she had overheard an argument between her mother and father when her mother accused her father of giving her a venereal disease. A bitter divorce resulted and her father quickly remarried, moved out of state, and gave up all rights to see Deidra. The deep wounds of rejection left her totally unable to talk about this emotional trauma in her life until the last weeks of her life. Then she finally had to admit having a "venereal" disease, **AIDS**, which she had contracted from one of her sexual partners. She had spent years denying the existence of the disease to her physical, emotional, and spiritual detriment.

Another common early reaction is shock. The outpouring of stress hormones, cortisol, and adrenalin, interacting with the autonomic nervous system, causes a virtual explosion of physical symptoms in response to an emotional event.[3] The heart speeds up and begins to skip beats, the breathing becomes faster and deeper, the skin turns cool and clammy, the mouth becomes dry, the stomach churns or becomes nauseated, and mental concentration improves—all from the interaction between the emotional areas in the midbrain and the rest of the nervous system. Bad health news seems to echo in the mind, blocking out further understanding and communications. These physical changes may be so intense that the person faints.

The types of emotional reactions found in grief are numerous and become more plentiful, more varied, and potentially more intense, as the reaction phase persists. The classic emotional defenses used during grief are reaction formation (feeling the opposite of what we should), suppression (pushing painful

137

situations out of our memory), rationalization (constructing a new reality where we are comfortable), repression (selective forgetfulness), and projection (displacing our hurt emotions onto another). Defenses are complex interactions between reality and emotions, where reality and pain are sacrificed to preserve emotional stability. These complex reactions may need counseling and psychotherapy if they do not resolve spontaneously within a few weeks.

Many more simple emotions are apparent during the reaction phase of grief. Anger, abandonment, betrayal, bitterness, crying, depression, despair, hysteria, loneliness, and others feelings are manifested in response to the perceived losses, the loss of a loved one, loss of a family member, or the impending loss of one's own life. Grief in more elementary terms is the emotional reaction brought on by actual or perceived loss. Our patients will grieve for themselves when they see that these losses, the loss of time, control, relationships, self-esteem, function, or role, each a precious commodity that is slipping away.[4] Fear of pain, loneliness, suffering, and abandonment add to the losses for ill persons. Their reserves of energy become depleted, and helplessness pushes them deeper into despair and depression. The comfort and presence of family and the loving guiding counsel from a pastor or counselor can bring peace out of confusion, reality out of defenses, support for the helpless, and spiritual strength to the weakened AIDS victim.

COUNSELING DURING THE REACTION PHASE

As a grief counselor, you may want to envision yourself as a firefighter. The analogy is surprisingly true. Counselors are called upon in crisis situations to put out emotional fires, some big, others small.

Most people don't call on their firefighters to see if their home is "fireproof." Most don't consult their firefighters to learn better ways to escape or prevent the blaze. Yet the greatest help a firefighter could possibly give would be information on how to prevent fires, how to protect the family during an accidental fire, how to escape, and how to inspect the house looking for areas at risk for burning.

Information given by the firefighter ahead of the crisis could prevent pain, suffering, and death. But not many people call their firefighter until the house is already ablaze. Most pastors and counselors have great expertise in preventing emotional problems, helping relationships through communication, diagnosing problem areas and emotional needs before they explode into flames, as well as other preventive counseling skills such as premarital counseling for the newly forming family. Family physicians, like myself, are well trained in the prevention of physical and emotional problems; but we are seldom afforded the opportunity to help before severe health problems are staring us in the face. In the many cases of AIDS, some preventative health education may have saved our patients from ever contracting the disease as well as the severe emotional turmoil that is unleashed by the reality of the infection.[5]

The emotional "firefighter" is needed in the early stages of grief, as AIDS patients will need help putting out their emotional "brushfires." Supportive counseling, around the time of diagnosis and for days to weeks afterward, should be offered to the patients and their families. Counselors' "extinguishers" offer hope where the doctors may have said no, comfort when the symptoms of AIDS are beginning to surface, and spiritual answers for the confusion as to "why."

Brushfires always uncover the forest floor, revealing hidden items and forgotten or discarded trash. Acute emotional reactions always uncover family dysfunctions, emotional needs, and personality characteristics that may have led to long-term psychological problems. Listen attentively for these problems, but remember your first and most important task is to give comfort and support until the emotional turmoil of the grieving process is calmed.

Grief reactions are as individual as the patient who grieves. If a patient has been through prior crisis experiences, then he or she will be better equipped to react with emotional restraint and cognitive stability in the face of a crisis situation or a severe illness. Those who are more mature are also more likely to fair well when the bad news is received. Yet I have seen devoted Christians break down into total hysteria when a health crisis looms; we must not judge their spiritual maturity on the basis of their "grief personality" alone.

Generally, however, the depth and length of the grief reaction depends upon the spiritual understanding of pain and suffering, the internalization of those beliefs, the maturity of the patient, and his or her prior experience with crisis.

The AIDS epidemic has spread through the homosexual community and those highly dependent on illicit drugs or sexuality to gratify their urges and pacify their anxieties. Each of these addictions breeds immature dependence on the sexual or drug object.[6] Addicts exhibit extremely self-centered behaviors when their cravings are reigning emotionally supreme. They perceive that the loss of their gratifying substance or activity will create an emotional withdrawal crisis that will intensify, complicate, and prolong the usual emotional reaction phase of grief. On the opposite side, many of these highly addicted individuals are also fatalistic in their attitudes toward life and death. With the knowledge that AIDS is a part of their life style, they may already have accepted their "death warrant," and show little concern or few emotional reactions during the early stages of grief. In these cases, spiritual answers for the questions previously raised about the "whys" and the "who really cares?" of their addiction may already have been shunned.

Though the range of emotional reactions in AIDS patients will be great, we must be sure that education about the facts related to the disease and its treatment are included in the early stages of grief. This often dispels the unnecessary images of destruction and pain patients initially feel. Reactions are dependent upon the patients' maturity, spiritual understanding, emotional needs, prior crisis experience, personality characteristics, and any knowledge about AIDS given to them.

Jay's case was illustrated in chapter one. He contracted AIDS about as unfairly as any patient I have seen, through a contaminated needle when he sought medical treatment in Haiti, where he was ministering with a church group. Let me offer you bits and pieces of our conversations during Jay's reaction phase and later as he moved toward accepting his plight and eventually growing in God's grace and in spiritual maturity.

Jay

The diagnosis of Jay's AIDS was made after a long illness with three different hospitalizations. The news that he had a fatal condition was not a shock to him. It was the agent of his fatal condition, AIDS, that caused the shock, paralysis, great spiritual and emotional turmoil. He never went through blatant denial. The night the doctor told him he had AIDS, a nurse on the floor came into the room and held Jay while he cried. After about an hour, she suggested, "Let's pray."

"I don't know if I would have made it through the night if it hadn't been for the nurse—I still don't know her name, just that she loved the Lord,"" Jay said.

"I simply can't believe that God could do this to me or to Darla (three students and Jay went to the clinic; now Jay and one other student named Darla had AIDS). It is so unfair," Jay complained.

"You made the choice to serve God wherever he called you. You chose to go to Haiti. You made the preparations. You raised the money, and you said 'Here I am, Lord; I'm willing. Scripture is clear that serving God carries bodily risk; but in return, it offers great spiritual reward," I answered.

"But, I never sinned like those homosexuals," Jay said.

"We're all sinners. You would have sinned against God if you knew you were supposed to go to Haiti, and then you refused. The sexually addicted homosexual men have sinned like each of us, each in their spiritual ignorance enslaved to their sinful lusts," I said.

"I feel so alone. I can't tell this to anyone. Everyone would stop being my friend if they knew I had AIDS," Jay said.

"You wouldn't want them as friends if they rejected you because of this," I said. (Up until Jay's death, over a year and a half after this conversation, Jay had revealed his plight to more than fifty people. Not one had rejected him. In fact, many of them became closer and were extremely supportive of him.)

"How can I tell my dad that I have AIDS? He's not saved and that will destroy my witness to him," Jay cried.

"Tell him the honest truth of how you got the disease. You'll just have to trust God that it will help instead of hurt your relationship," I said. Jay's relationship with his father improved greatly, and he was able to witness to him a number of times before he died.

"How can I handle the rest of my life, however long I have? Where will I live? Where will I work? How can God use me?" Jay asked.

"Once you have accepted that God knows what he is doing, then you will have those questions answered for you. The book of Romans tells us that God can use any illness, problem, heartache, or loss to bring us closer to him, and then move us to the ministry he desires for us. Only when we accept his plan for this tragedy, can we be given peace about the problem and 'marching orders' where he will continue to use us," I said.

Six months later Jay demonstrated his spiritual growth.

"God has given me a peace about the disease and has told me to work toward a ministry to drug abusers who are infected with AIDS. I believe this is where God wanted me in the first place; he just had to find a way to get me there," Jay told me.

Jay died while he was finishing his last classes in preparation for the ministry. His witness to his family and friends, however, had great spiritual impact.

COUNSELING TOWARD ACCEPTANCE

The process of grieving is never hard and fast. Most people who are shocked by a sudden loss or illness react to that situation with denial, anger, anxiety, and sadness, but then move toward accepting the reality of their loss. The more violent the initial emotional reaction, the less reality of the illness is cognitively understood.[7] But these protective emotional defenses are needed less and less as the problem is understood, accepted, and integrated into the reality of the person's life. Acceptance then is a two-fold process. First, the patient must cognitively understand and accept the reality of the loss. Second, the patient must integrate this new reality into his or her emotions and accept it as unchangeable. The scriptural model includes an all-important third step as well: acceptance of God's will and purpose as revealed through a situation or loss.

Secular counseling identifies those who persist in the various stages of reaction, and attempts to separate those who are pathologically fixed or stopped in the midst of their grief from those who are progressing normally toward acceptance of their new reality. Helping a grieving person to put aside his or her denial, to reverse his or her projection, and to work through his or her emotional needs is the goal of their work.[8] Acceptance becomes the goal to be achieved. It's almost like getting a person who is afraid of flying to walk into the plane—and then leaving him or her inside the door, instead of demonstrating to the person how and where to sit, how to relax during takeoff, where to focus his or her balance, and how to block out fears through thought diversion.

Acceptance brings comfort to the patient; but without the maturity gained by this emotional trial, it is useless. We must do more than push our phobic patient inside the door. Moving our grieving patient only to the point of acceptance leaves the job half-finished. Many people who originally work through their grief fall back into the reaction phase when more bad news is received or when their condition changes. As the airplane analogy goes, the door was left open and they just walked out of the plane, returning to their state of unresolved despair.

There is no spiritual meaning for grieving, suffering, or pain without a third phase: the phase of maturation and growth.[9] Thus, acceptance becomes a milestone in conquering the emotional consumption of the victim, but is not the ultimate goal in God's plan for that illness.

Christian counseling should differ greatly from the secular on this issue. Using the analogy of spiritual conversion as our template, acceptance, like making the decision for salvation, can lead to immediate growth. With neglect, without spiritual growth and maturation, grieving individuals will return to their pre-salvation emotional morass. We are just beginning to help our patients when they see God's purpose for suffering and God's will as manifested by AIDS in their lives. Though the discovery of AIDS creates a very frightening and insecure time, it is also creates a spiritual opportunity we must help our patients to grab.

When the patient has accepted the reality of AIDS, and has gained the necessary insight to properly put this problem into a larger understanding, then we must help him or her to

143

internalize what has been learned. We must inscribe upon his or her psyche the greater lessons that Scripture can teach through suffering. We must disciple these "converts" and help them to grow in faith and mature both emotionally and spiritually.[10]

COUNSELING TOWARD GROWTH AND MATURATION

Gaining insight into God's purpose for disease allows our patients to accept AIDS and mature into a less self-centered view of their disease and God's ultimate will. Yet this attitude needs to be fostered through a discipling relationship, much as a pastor disciples a young convert. The more our patients grow, the more positive their outlooks will be. The more positive the outlook, the less stress-damage occurs to the already crippled immune system.[11] As mentioned earlier, a number of important psychological studies have linked grieving and stress to reduced immune function.[12] Reduction of this damage should be a high priority for those counseling AIDS patients.

Jay was an excellent example of spiritual and emotional growth in the midst of the bodily deterioration of HIV disease. He put aside his denial, worked through his guilt and feelings of abandonment, accepted HIV disease as God's best course for his life, and matured as he trained for the ministry to drug addicts. His growth ground to a halt as he experienced an exacerbation of his disease, an infection that caused him to be hospitalized. The recurrence of guilt, depression, and anger during these times was understandable, and he was difficult to console. His outlook was as positive as could be expected in face of his deteriorating physique.

Despite this, Jay continued to grow and mature. Even to the end, he had an unshakable desire to minister to those dying from their addictions.

Most of us understand the counseling concept of emotional growth and maturity, but often cannot describe the exact psychodynamic changes that have occurred. These patients demonstrate a calmer, more self-assured attitude toward their negative situations. They look more toward helping others instead of rehearsing their own songs of self-pity. Emotional outbursts of anger or expressions of bitterness are gone or greatly improved.

Communication within their relationships is often improved instead of the opposite, so that the constant sapping of the strength of others in their support group becomes a thing of the past.

Counseling for emotional growth includes building self-esteem, sustaining hope of return to a near-normal life, and setting some achievable short-term goals for improving self and relationships.[13] We must continue to dissipate the guilt associated with AIDS, a venereal disease, away from our patients while remaining positive and supportive about their present abilities and plans. This helps them to rebuild their damaged self-esteem. Offering hope through cases of near-complete recovery from cancers, serious injuries, and even AIDS promotes the hope of recovery that is so vital to maintaining a positive outlook while reducing the damage of stress. Setting tangible relationship and communication goals with loved ones or friends, such as spending the weekend away with family, or taking a friend out for lunch, can foster emotional healing. Suggesting to our patients that they continue with exercise or walking programs while working on healthy eating habits can bring a positive future into their present thoughts.

Evidences of spiritual growth and maturation may be easily spotted or may be quietly hidden within the heart of our patient. Simply asking them to verbalize how God has used AIDS in them will allow them to openly proclaim the Spirit's teaching and their changed attitudes. We may see growth through further exacerbations and infections as their attitudes portray a peace that only God can give. The emotional and spiritual fruits are well worth our time and effort. Our discipling, along with the Spirit's intervention, can bring stability and comfort when their disease worsens, as well as delivering joy before their time of greatest sorrow.

COUNTERACTING GUILT, BITTERNESS, AND SELF-PITY

Here is an interesting conundrum. Our consciences seem to be intensely silent when our emotions push us into actions with consequences, but painfully noisy after we reap those consequences. Children who are always getting into trouble seem to know that they have done wrong—after the deed is done; but they seldom listen to their consciences before the wrongful acts are accomplished. The same incongruity exists in adolescents and adults. Once embroiled in an emotional relationship or situation, the volume of the "little voice" in their consciences seems to decrease until after they have enjoyed their rebellion. Then the volume returns and their "little voice" has a lot to say.

The human conscience, like pain, is a gift of God, a gift that distinguishes us from animals, a gift that is intended to protect and preserve, and yet a gift that keeps many separated from God, filled with bitterness and guilt.

The emotion of guilt is common for those who have engaged in sexual promiscuity whether they became infected with AIDS or not. Guilt will often follow a promiscuous young man or woman into marriage, resulting in mistrust, doubt, suspicion, and sexual dysfunctions such as premature ejaculation, vaginismus, and impotence. It can cause a wedge to form between marital partners that is hard to cover and easy to recognize.

Guilt is blame which we cast at ourselves for behaviors we regret. Bitterness is blaming others for their contribution to our problems. Each emotion levels blame for those involved in an improper action. Guilt points inward, blaming our own wrong motives or our faulty intellects. Bitterness points outwardly at the perceived wrong motives of others, their deficient intellects, or their depraved genes. These emotions are focusing on something or someone else instead of on the personal character flaw or the sinful nature that is inherent in all human beings.

> When tempted, no one should say, 'God is tempting me.' For God cannot be tempted by evil, nor does he tempt anyone; but each one is tempted when, by his own evil desire, he is dragged away and enticed. Then, after desire has conceived, it gives birth to sin; and sin, when it is fullgrown, gives birth to death. (James 1:13–15)

Those persons caught in the cycle of guilt and bitterness may resolve these emotions by accepting the free gift of forgiveness that is graciously given from a loving God. They can be counseled to refocus their emotions, to rethink the cause, and to desire a resolution. What specific acts or behaviors are the patients feeling guilt about? Why are they blaming someone else for consenting acts, acts that began out of love or affection? What communications have occurred between the infected persons and the individuals who have been accused as the AIDS carriers?

Guilt and bitterness result from a lack of forgiveness. Our patients must first seek to forgive themselves for making sexual mistakes, which are extremely common in our culture. They must also be willing to forgive the infecting parties. If an insatiable sexual appetite led the patients to become infected, then recognizing this lust as sin is paramount to seeking a spiritual resolution, and reaching out to God for his ultimate forgiveness and the improved health it brings.[14]

The act of sorting out the confused feelings, putting them aside with counseling, and moving toward forgiveness of self and others by seeking forgiveness from God will break the burden of bitterness and guilt.

DEPRESSION AND DISEASE

Chronic disease and depression are common bedfellows. Accordingly, HIV disease will often bring about depression, especially as many patients survive five to ten years after a diagnosis is made. That's five to ten years to contemplate their impending death. As with many forms of cancer, the surety of early death is present among HIV patients. Medications and alcohol used to calm these painful emotions often make depression worse, and may reduce the inhibitions against suicide.[15] As our patients will be under medical care for HIV, for infections associated with HIV, and probably for other medical symptoms and problems, they inadvertently may be given medications that will make their depression worse. Early recognition of depression that has been complicated by prescription or nonprescription medication is important in the overall course of AIDS counseling and treatment.

We know that HIV affects brain tissues through direct destruction of support cells (glial cells) or through toxin generation by infectious agents. This destruction leads to the psychiatric symptoms discussed in chapter 3, including dementia and paranoia; but it can lead to biochemical depression, as well.[16] The stresses of living with a chronic, fatal disorder precipitates

147

biochemical neurohormonal changes that give the physical and emotional symptoms of depression. The symptoms are weight loss or gain, early-morning awakening, flat or depressed emotions, depressed facial expressions, loss of sex drive, and suicidal thoughts.[17] Depression alone becomes an extreme source of stress on the HIV-positive person.

The depression associated with HIV disease should be detected as early as possible to prevent additional unnecessary stresses on the immune system. This will include early counseling, routine questioning for symptoms and signs, and referral for appropriate medical therapy as soon as the disease is detected. Explaining to the patient the need for early counseling and medication to preserve as much immune system function as possible usually enlists patient compliance and self-recognition of depressive symptoms.

RECURRENCE AND REJUVENATION

Infections and problems normally recur. Psychologically, our patients are gaining self-confidence, self-esteem, and control over their lives as they are recovering from the initial infection or symptoms. Reinfection causes the reappearance of guilt, anger, bitterness, denial, and many of the previous psychological reactions. Goals are set aside and the disappointment of not reaching them may bring further depression and disillusionment. The upward psychological slope toward rejuvenation makes a sharp and decided downturn with each recurrence of illness. (See Figure 8–1).

Prior preparation for disease recurrences should be a fundamental part of thorough counseling for AIDS. Making sure our patients understand what HIV is, how it affects the immune system, and what happens when the immune system is not strong enough to function is basic information. Patients should be told to report any fevers, skin lesions, cough, or changes in sensations to their physicians. Encouragement to take the prophylactic medications for HIV on a regular basis should be offered; but you can help them to prevent excessive guilt when a dosage is missed by suggesting, "everyone misses a dose or two now and then."

Basic education and information is important, and opens the door to discussions of emotional preparation for recurrences.

Recurrent Illness
Graphic Depiction of Losses During Illness and Recurrent Illness

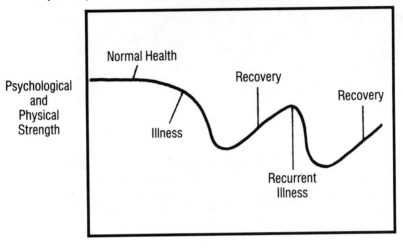

Time

Figure 8-1

How would you feel if your disease got worse? What preparations have you made? How much support will your family give you? Do you have any spiritual support? Would you blame yourself for an infection when it comes? Would you blame someone else? How do you feel about your doctor, the hospital, the place you receive your medical care? What do you believe will be the course of your disease? When do you think you will be too sick to work? How will you cope if you are sick from now until the time you die?

Helping our patients to think through and verbalize their feelings about the illness and care before they must be treated for an acute problem will help them to rehearse their response and cope better with reality. Even though we must admit AIDS will claim our patients sooner or later, we can instead stress emotional rejuvenation through our positive, supportive counseling, and emotional preparation for health events that are unfortunately inevitable, especially as they move into their terminal phase of the illness.

CHAPTER NINE

COUNSELING THE TERMINALLY ILL

William

The weather outside of the large, hermetically sealed hospital window was crystal clear with bright sunshine and the faintest aromas of spring. It was one of those March afternoons when the clear outline of the Blue Ridge Mountains could be seen in the distance. Ten-year-old William longed to be hiking along those ancient mountain trails. Instead he was hospitalized—again—for medical treatments and injections prescribed for his hemophilia.

A few days before this admission he had developed a high fever and cough and had been taken to the emergency room. A chest x-ray revealed a serious bilateral pneumonia, and he was promptly admitted. Antibiotics were started, but after twelve hours they didn't seem to be helping. A smear of his sputum held the answer, but his doctor said they wanted to wait on the culture and draw some other blood samples. William was also started on some special antibiotics and aerosols.

"I'm afraid that our suspicions were correct," the physician told William solemnly after he had been given the culture results.

"You mean I have AIDS?" William said.

"Yes. How did you know we suspected that?" the physician asked.

"I read a lot. There was an article in a news magazine that my parents get at home that described hemophiliacs like me getting AIDS and being treated with Bactrim for pneumonia. I just put two and two together," William stated.

"For a ten-year-old, you're pretty sharp," the physician said.

William's parents, who were also there, had known that HIV infection was a good possibility. After William was born and they found out he was a hemophiliac, they decided to not take any more risks by having other children. They invested all their time and energy into William, knowing that he could die from bleeding at any time. He was the Lord's and was always in his hands.

Surprisingly, they showed little emotion at the time HIV was confirmed. They quietly sat with the physician and asked a number of very informed, and intelligent questions about the future. Should he be on any medication? Has it been approved yet for children? What signs of infection should they look out for? How could they keep him as healthy as possible to prevent problems?

William had been switched to heat-treated Factor VIII almost two years earlier to try to prevent him from contracting HIV. One previous HIV titer had been negative. However, they also knew that it was still possible for William to have been infected with HIV prior to the switch. They had left it in God's hands.

"If this were my child," the physician said, "I don't believe I would have taken this tragic news so well."

"We are simply trusting in God to take care of him. That may

151

be here on earth or in heaven with our Savior. We can't second guess his decision," William's mother told the physician. She then had the opportunity to share the gospel with the physician and William's nurse.

The infection seemed to improve at first, then the fevers returned. William became more short of breath. He sensed that this was a serious setback. Fear of death was not his major concern, although he did express concern about pain. He wanted to make sure that the money he had earned last summer on his paper route, money he was saving for college, would be used at the hospital to provide some Bibles and tracts for other children on his floor. Some of the young patients he had met were dying from cancer.

He also wanted to make sure that he told his parents that he loved them and would look forward to being with them in heaven.

Within hours, a tube had to be placed in his lungs to help him breathe. He just didn't have enough strength to keep pushing for every breath. The infection continued to clog his breathing passages until even the machine could not keep William in this world.

He died of pneumonia eleven days after his admission, eight days after his family learned that he was HIV positive. William's mother and father thanked God that he did not suffer a painful death. And they thanked God for the ten wonderful years William had spent with them.

It was a pleasure to have known William, and to have seen a shining example of how a terminal illness should be handled, with spiritual maturity of the remarkable patient and his family. Despite his young age, William's spiritual maturity was evident in how he handled his hemophilia, the real testing ground before his death with HIV. Both parents were in full-time Christian work and had invested themselves in giving William the best quality time possible because they had to be prepared for any eventual illness. They had to practice daily how to give their worries, fears, and concerns about William to the Lord. By the grace they showed during his death, William's mother and father were obviously well practiced in giving to God what belonged to Him.

I don't know many families or patients who need our help as little as this family did. Yet their Christian friends made visits to the hospital, sent notes of encouragement, and kept them in their prayers constantly. We are all called to give comfort, care, and love as often as a crisis is seen. This example in our counseling will lead to a greater ministry through a local church or through our community, an example that is well pleasing to the Father.

TERMINAL ILLNESS AND HIV

No more difficult time exists, nor is there a more sorrowful moment than when a family receives the news that a disease is terminal. What does that mean? How much time does the patient really have? Is there no hope for survival from this disease?

According to our best scientific knowledge, AIDS is a disease that is 100 percent fatal. That means that given enough time, each person who is HIV positive will eventually die from infections or tumors associated with that disease. There is always the possibility that a small percentage, one to two percent, will survive well beyond expectations. This is true for all terminal illnesses. A small possibility exists that an HIV patient will die of another disease, an auto accident, suicide, or by some other means before AIDS will claim him or her. A few may die of sudden, unexpected, and unexplainable causes, which might be attributable to AIDS if we understood how HIV affects each part of the body. However, science is far from perfect and, in many cases, is not very accurate. The general public, physicians, and even scientists put more faith in science than it deserves.

When physicians diagnose a disease, whether it's cancer, heart disease, emphysema, or AIDS, we use statistics to guide our estimate of "longevity." A certain prognosis for cancer may suggest that most patients will be dead from their disease within six months. A few may die within days to weeks from our pronouncement of "six months to live." Others will live longer—between four to eight months. A very few may survive years after a serious tumor has been found because of spontaneous remission (which means that the tumor disappears for some reason, some medically explainable and others by unknown means). However, a majority of patients die within the expected time

153

frame. The prognosis can never be more accurate because of so many variables and individual factors.

Once HIV has been discovered, the prognosis is still bleak, even though medications have been found that may prolong the life of the sufferer. The future may hold some methods of completely eradicating the body of these viral particles, but not all patients will receive help once it is available. The helping professions must still deal with the emotional reactions toward AIDS.

EMOTIONAL REACTIONS TO TERMINAL ILLNESS

Few psychological problems have been as well studied over the past three decades as the grief reaction. Elisabeth Kübler-Ross is by far the most famous psychiatrist who has studied grief in dying patients and families. Her famous five stages of death and dying are now common teaching in classes dealing with grieving or death.[1] But even the science behind these observational studies holds inaccuracies. That is why there are still a number of competing "theories" of grieving that are espoused in the secular psychology literature.[2]

In almost all patients, a terminal illness will produce a grief reaction in the sufferer and in those within the patients' support systems. Emotional reactions during the initial times of grieving include denial, anger, isolation, bargaining, depression and sadness, shock, despair, numbness, abandonment, and loneliness. Many of the patients discussed previously expressed denial when they were given the news; many declared anger at their sexual partners, and at themselves for their own sexual mistakes. The volatile issues of promiscuity, addiction, and homosexuality convey a greater explosiveness to the initial reactions of AIDS patients or their sexual partners. As discussed in earlier chapters, we can expect to be dealing with very severe emotional reactions whenever we are dealing with a terminal AIDS patient.

The reality of mortality is precipitated when a mortal illness becomes worse. Our HIV patients are likely to survive a number of serious or even life-threatening infections during the first three to five years of the illness. Eventually, though, their strength to resist infection and keep up with daily activities will diminish.[3] They may be admitted over and over again to the hospital, or they may be weakened to the point of needing nursing-home care. A serious infection superimposed on a devitalized shell will likely bring emotional cracks or even shattering. In the midst of these severe emotional reactions, our caring and supportive counseling can help to hold the remaining pieces together.

Where can we focus our counseling efforts when patients are terminally ill? Our patients hopefully will have rehearsed their emotional reactions prior to the worsening episode of illness, so a simple reminder of the causes of their anger or frustration and how it was handled earlier in the illness will bring many to resolution. However, their constellation of reactions may present themselves differently with each recurrence of illness, even in the final stages. Whereas denial and anger were the prime expressions early in the illness, now we may be dealing with feelings of loneliness and depression. Helping patients to identify specific emotions, the reasons for those emotions, and then just letting them talk will allow them to work through their reactions as quickly and as comfortably as possible. A sympathetic demeanor, a hand to hold, a listening ear, and a minimum of directives about grieving tasks will gently support and guide them through an acute emotional reaction triggered by thoughts of a terminal episode.

Over the next days, weeks, or even months, the patient will need more than just a sympathetic ear, however. After a reasonable period of listening to their grief, our support must turn into positive encouragement, always looking at the benefits instead of the burdens, seizing opportunities instead of sinking into depression. We shouldn't dwell on the scriptures concerning death, but quickly switch to the comfort that will be obtained, the relationship that will be ours, the victories that will be won. Bringing hope even in these final hours can greatly relieve the inevitable self-pity and sadness that may come naturally, but shouldn't be allowed to diminish the joyful transition to our permanent home in heaven.

CARE IN TERMINAL ILLNESS

Patient needs created by the epidemic of AIDS are straining the very foundations of medical care in this country, especially in dealing with the needs of dying patients.[4] Those health-care professionals who have been closely following this explosion of new patients have wisely sought alternatives to the standard hospital environment for the many who will be ill and dying of AIDS during the next decades. The options of home care, hospice care, and nursing-home care have become more available and present a less expensive option in providing comfort and adequate medical care during a terminal illness such as AIDS.[5]

Home care for AIDS patients is becoming popular because of the cost factors and the close proximity to other supportive family members. Many insurance companies are now paying for nursing care at home, as well as medical supplies and appliances. Insurers have realized that these alternatives are a tremendous cost savings, compared with hospital or nursing-home care. And familiar surroundings are often the most comfortable for a severely ill or dying patient. This option builds family interdependence and often improves communication between members. However, dealing with an extremely sick individual can also stress the family to the point of explosion. An extremely supportive and available family is the prerequisite for attempting care at home. And regular means of relieving family members from their work with the AIDS victim is just as important.

Many AIDS patients will be forsaken by their families and friends simply because of a life style that led to contracting the disease or because family members fear catching the disease. That's where hospice programs and "buddy" programs can provide help where families cannot or will not. Hospice programs are well-organized plans for dealing with a dying patient at home. The program assigns a trained volunteer to befriend the patient, and guide him or her through the slow and painful downhill course, while comforting the family and helping the terminally ill patient die with dignity. Similarly, "buddy" programs assign a noninfected person to become a supportive friend for an AIDS victim. The "buddy" can just be available to talk, or to help with chores, correspondence, meals, or other tasks.[6] A relationship can be formed early, when there are few symptoms or problems, or later as the AIDS patient is losing many of his or her functions. Support is what is needed and provided by these programs.

Some patients require more intensive care that can only be given in the setting of a nursing home. No one wants to be placed in a nursing home when adequate care can be given at home by the family. But there are limits to the availability of home nurses, hospital beds, and specialized care, such as injectable medications, constant turning in bed, feeding tubes and other treatments that are only available in a nursing home. Some nursing homes have refused HIV-positive patients out of fear that other residents will be moved by their families, or by their own choice, to other facilities where no AIDS patients have yet been admitted. However, state laws are being put in place that restrict discrimination against HIV patients, making it easier for them to receive the care that is needed during their terminal phase.

John

"I have always been in control," he repeated to himself over and over. John was a fifty-six-year-old police officer, who had been wounded in the line of duty. After receiving six units of blood to stabilize his punctured liver, he had undergone six hours of surgery. The bleeding persisted, but the escaping blood was sucked out of his abdomen by drains that had been left in place. By the time the bleeding stopped, he had been given a total of fifteen units of blood. Amazingly, he survived and even went back to work.

Four years later, John developed a rare type of meningitis. Through further testing he was found to be HIV positive. He was treated but continued to lose weight.

Now's the best time for me to check out, he thought.

His wife was staying with her sister for a few days so he knew that the house would be quiet. He made sure that his will had been updated and notarized. He checked to make sure that his insurance premiums had been paid up. All the equipment that belonged to the department was returned to his locker at work, where it would be found. He wrote some loving notes for his two children and a six-page note to his wife. He called her in Philadelphia to make sure she was well and to tell her that he loved her and missed her.

With everything in order, he pulled out one of the vinyl body bags often used for victims of fatal crimes. He cleaned up the entire house. Then, after taking a large dose of sleeping pills, he slipped himself into the body bag which he had placed on the bed. That's how his wife found him two days later when she returned.

She was grateful that he called her before he died, and that he had died the way he wanted—in control.

PREPARATION FOR DEATH

When our patients reach the terminal phase in their disease, they will have put aside many of the complicating tasks and relationships that induce emotional pain. Their sole concentration will be on correcting, placing in order, and letting go. If they are fortunate enough to have a chance to apologize, express love, ask forgiveness, and renew relationships, then they will have some degree of peace. Settling financial matters, making funeral arrangements, finishing any business matters, and ensuring help for loved ones after their death gives patients the ability to control their final days. Once relationships are mended and control has been exercised over business matters, the terminal patient often begins letting go. Acceptance of impending death is much easier when these areas have been handled.

As always, our counseling in these final days should be supportive and positive. Words of encouragement about their decisions, about their medical care, their financial plans or will arrangements, their relationship efforts, and stressing a need for a closer relationship with their God should be offered to these patients. We must be sensitive to their needs for rest and solitude if they are in discomfort. In addition, the emotional needs of the family members must be met. In the face of eternity, a few extra moments spent in spiritual encouragement may have eternal consequences.

Jerry

Lying in the hospital bed he was sure would be his last, Jerry knew he was forgiven by a Savior who had died a more horrible and stigmatized death than the one Jerry himself was now facing. Jerry had accepted responsibility for the vile life style that had led to his HIV infection, and for the last year and a half he had shared his story with anyone who would listen, especially the part concerning his spiritual conversion. But his strength had been steadily eroding. Between May and July he had lost more than thirty pounds, and now he seemed to pick up a new infection every few days.

Jerry's parents, the Iowa farm family described earlier, had never forgiven him for his homosexual affairs. Instead, they had disowned him. "Just ship your AIDS-ridden body to China for all we care," his father had said. It was a dagger that twisted into his chest every time Jerry thought of his family's rejection. He could not forgive himself for the "pain" and "understandable shame" he had brought to his parents. Calling them again was out of the question. He couldn't stand to be rejected again.

His breathing was more labored, and it was difficult for him to keep alert. Then the phone ringing next to his bed seemed to energize his mostly skeletal frame.

"Jerry, it's your mom and dad," Jerry's father spoke timidly. "I had an interesting dream last night that I thought we should share with you. I was in a hospital bed, dying of AIDS. It looked like I was in a tunnel, but I still knew it was the hospital. All I could hear were people saying ugly things about me. They just seemed to be voices swirling about my bed. I didn't see any faces. Then an angel came down the tunnel. 'Why are these people so angry with me? I don't even known them,' I asked the angel. 'Have you forgiven them?' the angel asked me. Then a peace came over me, the voices stopped, and I woke up.

"I know, Jerry, that God sent that dream to wake me and your mom up. We love you no matter what you've done. God is giving us the strength to forgive you. We love you! Please forgive us for our hate," Jerry's father said.

"When you're out of the hospital, we want you to come home and live with us," Jerry's mother added.

"I love you both," was all he could say as tears rolled down his cheeks.

God's timing was perfect. Jerry's spirits were lifted and every one of the nurses could see the difference. Later that night, Jerry died, more at peace than he had been at any time since his conversion. He was able to forgive himself, just as his parents had forgiven him.

Healing and Acceptance

The comfort we can bring through our counseling near the time of death can still be healing and restorative. Sadly, there are often hidden grudges, skeletons in the closets of many family relationships in which forgiveness has not yet penetrated. These are the dying regrets that many terminal patients offer to their pastors, counselors, nurses, or physicians.

"Why couldn't my brother forgive me?" one asks. Or another cries in anguish, "I can't stand the thought of dying without telling my daughter." AIDS patients have to deal with the hidden and unspoken pain they have brought upon family and friends. Even when they know a loving Savior has forgiven them, they still ache to be forgiven by others who have been disappointed in them.

Taking the time and effort to heal these fractured relationships in the final hours of AIDS patients' lives delivers the best gift possible to the grieving patients. With their permission, we can attempt to talk with any member of the family who has been mentioned, seeking a reconciliation. Once the wounded family members consent to be reconciled, ask them to send a brief note or make a short call, just to let the patients know that all is forgiven, all is forgotten, and that the emotional pain is gone. The relief this offers to our patients will be like a morphine drip to the cancer sufferer, a medication that will take away all the pain.

Use of anticipatory counseling for the patients with their families present can give family members an opportunity to share their feelings about the death of their loved ones and allow them to settle any unresolved differences. Talking specifically about the funeral arrangements, services, and plans for mourning or celebration opens the emotional door to discuss feelings about these practices. A dying son or daughter may be able to share his or her new faith with family, proclaiming death as a celebration instead of a sorrow-filled event. Feelings about each other that are often not shared at any other time can be revealed at this type of family gathering. The experience and maturity, as well as a profound new understanding of dying, is gained by family members that are present during the death of another member. It is an experience that will not be forgotten by family members, and one that can, with some guidance, be an extremely positive one.

Terminal illness represents the greatest opportunity we will have for offering spiritual healing to our patients. If they have not yet accepted the free gift of God's grace, we should be faithful stewards in taking care of God's business. Even if they are Christians, gently asking them if they are sure, if they are ready, should not be too difficult for either ourselves or for them. Helping the patients to repair their relationships with Christ during the final hours of life can assure them of a home "not made with hands." The physical needs of the patients are important and the psychological comfort of the patients are our life's work; but we must not neglect that which God holds more dear than the life of his beloved Son, the soul of each and every patient whom God has entrusted to us.

EUTHANASIA/SUICIDE

Our societal preference has been changing over the last few years toward more patient control of the dying process instead of the present medically controlled death. Instruments such as respirators, endotracheal intubations, intravenous lines, monitors, nasogastric tubes, hospital beds, and injections are the medical paraphernalia many people have grown to fear. These lifesaving technologies are inordinately associated with prolonging disease, pain, suffering, and death.[7] Patients no longer implicitly trust physicians to always do what is best for them during their final days and hours; they fear that medical care may prolong their suffering.

There is great confusion as to what can be done to relieve the suffering of a loved one without committing an ethical misdeed or a criminal act simply through ignorance. Some are afraid to allow a family member to die at home because they might be accused of murder or neglect. (See Figure 9–1 for the definitions of common terms associated with death, dying, suicide, and euthanasia.)

Within a few decades, the era of modern medical technology has risen with all its lifesaving and life-prolonging devices. But now the pendulum is swinging back the other way. Many persons

Definitions of Premature Death

Euthanasia. To help a dying patient die prematurely.

Passive Euthanasia. A physician, family member, or friend gives to the patient the ability to prematurely end his or her life, and the patient uses that means to do so.

Active Euthanasia. A physician, family member, or friend actually administers a medication in an excessive dosage with the intent of relieving a dying patient's suffering by quickly ending his or her life.

Mercy Killing. A spouse, family member, or friend uses some means, violent or medical, to kill a sick or dying individual prematurely.

Suicide. Premature death by an individual, caused by violent or medical means used on himself or herself. The person may be ill, dying, depressed, or suffering from other psychiatric illnesses.

Heroic Measures. The various medical treatments used to keep severely ill people from dying. The usual means considered heroic consist of respiratory support via an endotracheal tube and ventilator; blood pressure maintenance through medications; heart rhythm through temporary pacemakers, medications, and counterpulsation balloon pumping; kidney function through dialysis; and feedings through gastrostomy tubes or by intravenous hyperalimentation. Routine measures include standard medications for heart, lungs, and kidneys, nasogastric feedings, intravenous fluids, antibiotics, and oxygen by mask. Minimal measures would include intravenous fluids and some form of nutrition without the use of medications, oxygen, catheters, or monitors.

Withdrawal of Medical Treatment. If a patient is dying, the family or patient may decide to withdraw any and all medical care. This usually includes oxygen, monitors, and many or all medications. Food, intravenous fluids, or fluid by mouth should not be considered medical treatment.

Neglect. When one person withholds medical care, food, or protection from another, resulting in the dependent person's physical or emotional depravation or injury. The dependent one may be a child, a sick individual, or an elderly and infirm person.

Figure 9–1

have witnessed the discomfort of a loved one whose suffering seemed to be prolonged instead of eased by medical technology. The trend is returning now to the more conservative ethic which allows a patient to control his or her own death among family members who are supportive and present, at home in familiar surroundings with his or her dignity intact.[8]

The ethical pitfalls, however, of a patient-controlled death are obvious. Controversy surrounds the physician from

Michigan, an active member of the Hemlock Society (a right-to-die organization), who recently created a "suicide machine," offering patients a painless, clean, and swift way of killing themselves. He then used the medicinal-delivery device on a patient who was in the early stages of Alzheimer's disease. Though the patient desired to die, the physician was responsible for the medications that ultimately ended her life. This represents a strong move toward active euthanasia in the United States.

Where is the line between withdrawal of medical care and euthanasia? What is the difference between active and passive euthanasia? Should an AIDS patient have the medical option of "assisted suicide"? With the cost of medical care skyrocketing, wouldn't it be less expensive to handle those with AIDS as they wish, to allow them to commit assisted euthanasia or suicide? Where can we ethically draw the line?

When the patient is terminally ill and desires death, assisting him or her in committing suicide by obtaining medication for an overdose, by injecting a lethal dosage into their vein, or by shooting them with a pistol can all be considered active euthanasia. "We are just ending their suffering," some might say.

The Netherlands has laws that allow physicians to assist terminally ill patients with their desire to die, and other countries have considered passing similar legislation. For those in the terminal stages of AIDS, many have and will desire the help of someone to end their lives more quickly, while they are still in control. But this ethic has not yet been adopted by public opinion or by the laws of the United States. A number of mercy killers have been convicted of murder.

However, we ethically allow dying patients to be withdrawn from medications, treatments, surgery, or even from food and water at their command. It is a privilege of our free society, and often the last rational and coherent wish of these patients. The line between withdrawing medical care, such as withdrawing patients from life support when they are unable to make that decision, and withdrawing vital treatments at patient request has become blurred with active euthanasia. The demand to make these decisions will continue to grow as many young persons will be dying with AIDS.

And where is the line drawn between the patient deciding to prohibit a painful treatment and opting instead to take extra medication, possibly committing suicide by doing so? When they are not terminally ill, those who desire to commit suicide are protected by our society, and kept from harming themselves. In contrast, we presently allow those suffering physically from a painful situation to relieve their suffering (and usually speed up their deaths) by withdrawing from medical care. But we do not allow those who are suffering psychologically to end their pain. Is this fair?

We will be called upon in our professional role to offer spiritual wisdom and scriptural principles for these difficult questions, especially as we advise AIDS patients.

For those with AIDS, as with any terminal disease, suicide or asking someone for assistance with suicide is wrong. Scripture does not support mercy killing or active euthanasia. Both the Old and New Testaments are clear about causing death to another. (See Exodus 20:13 and 21:12; Leviticus 24:17; and Matthew 5:21.) The Bible even answers the questions of those who desire death; God rejected their wishes. (See Job 30:20–23 and Psalm 88.) The Bible also offers the reminder that God "will not let you be tempted beyond what you can bear" (1 Cor. 10:13). He knows exactly what he is doing by allowing pain, whether physical or psychological. We need to see those purposes through his eyes and with his eternal understanding.

Though Jesus was convicted and suffered unfairly for our sins, he did not squirm or shirk his eternal responsibility (Phil. 2:8). Our patience should be the same and we should accept suffering as a means of growing closer to him who suffered for us. Whether we are dying of AIDS because of promiscuous activity for which we are responsible, or whether we have become infected through innocent means, by transfusion or needle stick, we still have a responsibility to God to allow sickness and suffering to shape us into the image of Christ.

Are we being cruel by saying we must all suffer? Does that mean we should reject the use of pain medications as Christ rejected the sponge soaked with a drug on the cross? (See John 19:29.)

The use of pain medications by mouth or by vein, when given at proper dosages, can relieve the dying patient of virtually all pain and suffering. There is no scriptural directive against giving comfort, but for the opposite. The Samaritan gave comfort, aid, transportation, money, and a pledge of further assistance if needed when he found a man wounded by the sin of others (Luke 10:30–37). God gave us the intellectual abilities to improve our care for the suffering and dying from a physical standpoint. He also calls us to minister psychological care during this time, through supportive counseling from Scripture and through stressing the positive aspects of suffering for his purpose.

However, we must be careful not to judge weaker brothers or sisters who decide they are unable to trust God for strength and grace during their physical demise. We have all failed in trusting him fully for enough faith at one time or another. As well, we should never condemn suicide in front of a family who just lost a loved one by this manner of death. Many good Christian men and women, in times of emotional weakness and depression, have committed suicide while terminally ill. Would God reject those who earnestly believe that is the best solution for them? Would God condemn those who have placed their eternal trust in him? However, Scripture suggests the better path is to trust God for the ability to die in his perfect timing, not in our timing (Eccles. 3:2).

Lines can be drawn through these ethical questions from scriptural examples and admonitions. Active euthanasia and mercy killing is wrong in all situations; God does not support our killing unless it's in self-defense or in defense of our family or nation.

Though the line between active and passive euthanasia is unclear, passive euthanasia by withdrawing medical care is presently allowed by law. It may be considered the best decision for an informed patient, a decision that is between God and the patient. Food and water, however, is not medical treatment, but a means of giving comfort to the sick and infirm. Though the courts have allowed the withdrawal of food and fluids, and though the American Medical Association considers withdrawal of food and fluids as ethical treatment, it is merely a normal and humane act that should not be stopped. However, forced feedings through tubing against the patient's wishes could prolong family suffering and can be considered unnecessary, especially if the patient is already brain dead.[9]

Suicide is not the best decision as far as Scripture is concerned, but within the consciences of the dying individuals is a decision made between themselves and God.

No matter what the terminal decision is, no matter if it is ethically, professionally, or scripturally right or wrong, giving comfort is a ministry that each of us can perform during and following the death of a family member. It is a higher calling than being ethically correct. It is a higher calling than being dogmatic about a hazy area of Scripture. It should be our ministry to emulate Jesus Christ as he ministered comfort and healing to the multitudes that followed him.

CHAPTER TEN

COUNSELING THE FAMILIES
OF AIDS PATIENTS

Elizabeth

"How did your family feel about your contracting AIDS?" I asked. Elizabeth had been admitted for a severe case of shingles with fever and spread of the blisters all over her body. I talked with her the day she was to be discharged from the hospital.

"At first it wasn't easy," she said. "Even though I am just about finished with college, my little brother and sister, and my mother, have relied upon me a lot since my father left about eight years ago. I was often the one who cleaned the house, fixed dinner, and made sure the younger kids did their homework and got to bed on time."

"What led you into using drugs?" I asked.

"When I was sixteen, about two years after Dad left, I got real down about having to take care of everyone. That was when I met Jacob. We had a sexual relationship, and he got me some pills and later some other drugs to make me feel better. It was easy after injecting them to keep craving them. But I stopped without too much problem."

"Did you ever pick up any diseases from your boyfriend?" I queried.

"They thought I had hepatitis once and said it could be from my boyfriend or the drugs. It only lasted a few weeks," she said.

"When did you find out about the AIDS infection?" I asked.

"That was about four years later, in my junior year in college. I had this real bad infection in my mouth that just wouldn't go away. My dentist sent me to a specialist and he diagnosed it after a few days and some blood testing. He wasn't sure how I got the infection since I had had a few other boyfriends and since I had used drugs."

"How did you tell your mother?" I asked.

"Fortunately, I didn't have to. Since the divorce she was always working two jobs, but she took the afternoon off to come with me to the doctor's office. He told her and he answered all her questions," Elizabeth stated.

"How did she take the news?" I asked.

"She didn't talk to me for a week. All she did was blame my father for leaving so she had to work so hard to support us. She finally talked with me about sex, but I already knew most of what she said. My younger brother and sister and my mother, we just seemed to grow farther and farther apart. It wasn't until I had been hospitalized a couple of times before she really opened up and started to be supportive. We got some counseling while we were in the hospital and that helped," she said.

"What about your brother and sister?" I asked.

"They still don't go in my room or touch any of my stuff," she said with a slight chuckle.

THE ROLE OF THE FAMILY

AIDS is a disease that afflicts many young persons who are not dependent upon a family for physical or emotional support.

The initial epidemic has been spread by emancipated homosexual men and IV drug users, individuals who have made unfortunate life-style choices that families often find repugnant. Families grieve for these young men who have become so addicted to their pleasurable promiscuity that their judgment has become clouded, and their desire for family consolation has evaporated.

The epidemic, however, has now changed directions and is headed straight for the center of the family. HIV is now spreading into young and promiscuous men and women in their high-school or early-college years. By the time they develop symptoms of HIV disease, many will be married and having children. Without a cure or adequate vaccine soon, the next generation of families, mothers, fathers, and children will be the victims of this growing epidemic.

Beside the emotional support families provide to adolescents, they are also the most important source for prevention of AIDS. Families today are the battle line for facing this disease head on. They are fighting to keep their children from the dangers of premature sexuality and drug addiction.[1] They are beginning as never before to discuss sexuality with their adolescent children.[2] Family members are becoming involved with school and church educational programs designed to equip our young people to abstain from promiscuity and drugs. And the battle will continue well into the next century.

We would be facing a serious epidemic even if only a few hundred people were infected and dying. We presently have a few hundred thousand who are ill, and a few million who are infected. The role of the family in preventing, guiding, directing, and supporting those young persons who are at risk for HIV is immense, and we should do everything we can as health-care professionals to enlist and educate families to be a part of the solution.

FAMILY REACTION TO AIDS

The family is also where a fallen member retreats for comfort and support. When a family hears of the illness of one member, we can expect tears of grief to be shed. The family and the grieving individual react with the same psychological mechanisms which are devised to protect the ability to deal with reality. Each member of the family will grieve in his or her own personal way, based on prior experiences, personality patterns, and present emotional state.[3] Added to the individual grieving patterns are the group patterns for grief: how any specific family reacts when together, demonstrating it unique "group" personality.

The initial individual reactions to grief are predictable. A shock-like reaction produces the initial sensations that people often associate with grief: "My heart stopped," or "everything just felt frozen," are common reactions. A rapid flush of adrenalin, increases in heart rate, breathing rate, and shut down of the intestines leads to most of these early sensations.[4] Denial, or the disbelief of this kind of tragic news, lets the reacting person deal with that reality in a more controlled way. Hysterical reactions, crying and screaming, shouting of incoherent pleas, can be the emotional result of a totally unprepared parent or spouse.

The group's initial emotional reactions may be the same as the leading member of that group, in the case of a family, probably a mother or father. Or it may exhibit some of the dysfunctional qualities that have led to individual psychological problems. For example, a family that requires drinking, drug, or sexual problems to provide motivation for family stability may become violently angry as a group, and focus that anger at the sick member. Another, maternally dominated family may react divergently as a group, the mother giving the needed care and support for the AIDS patient, while the rest of the family becomes more apathetic and more distant from the sick individual.

Part of the initial reaction to a loved one's illness depends upon the knowledge of HIV that each member has obtained. Individual and group emotional reactions will be tempered depending on the more prior knowledge, and the fewer biases each member has. The majority of information in the hands of the general public makes AIDS appear as an immediate death threat where no hope is possible. But hope does exist for those who are detected early, started on medication, followed closely for changes, and might possibly live long enough to reap the benefits of better treatments or a cure in the next decade or two, or three.[5] The more fatal the family members believe the final outcome will be, the stronger their emotional reactions will be.

As discussed in the last chapter, loss is the reason people grieve. Grieving mothers and fathers, however, are not just reacting to the possible loss of their children; they are seeing many more intangible losses, as well. They will lose the relationship and protection children offer their parents in old age. They will lose a part of posterity, a hope for generations to come. They will lose their investment of time, of love, and of sharing. And in families where AIDS is claiming a small son or daughter, they are losing these things to a stigmatized disease. For those living in the time of Christ, an analogous loss would have been losing a son or daughter to the stigmatized disease of leprosy, or dying a stigmatized death on a Roman cross. (See Isaiah 33:12, Deuteronomy 21:23, and Galatians 3:13.)

Even though many persons afflicted with AIDS are now grown adults and are living separately from their nuclear families, the emotional reactions by distant family members may be just as intense. In other families, the depth of grief among the separated family members may be very shallow. Conflicts about life-style choices or parental disappointment may further distance the separated adult children from their parents.[6] Grief, however, will be expressed and may be the vehicle for reconciliations between estranged members of the family. It's a shame that it often takes some grievous problem to reopen lines of communication.

We must remember that other family members besides adult children can be infected as well. The middle-aged father, breadwinner, and family leader who received transfusions of HIV-infected blood during abdominal surgery may be dying of AIDS. The baby girl born to a mother with HIV will soon experience the viral destruction of her immune system. The single woman, a career medical missionary in Africa, may be home on furlough for medical treatment. Young and old, parents and children, all may succumb to the disease, leaving other family members to grieve. Grandparents, parents, and children—anyone can be infected.

As we begin to deal with the emotional reactions of the family touched by HIV, we need to remember the basics. First, we should assess the level of understanding and information that has been given to them by their physician or other sources. Then we should answer their questions and make sure their information is adequate. This will ensure that all unnecessary fears and concerns are put aside.

Next, we must assess the relationships within the family and the quality of problems within those relationships. Identifying the relationship problems and helping family members to gain insights into their relationships with the HIV victims will equip them to be more supportive of each other, as well as the patient. Finally, we should discuss family members' initial reactions and feelings toward the illness, guiding them through the normal course of grief. We can suggest early their need to accept what has happened so they will be able to give stronger support for their family's sick member.

COMPLICATING ISSUES

The choices, hidden motives, and even silent addictions of one or more family members can greatly complicate the early grieving reactions and the eventual family support that is offered to HIV patients. These complicating issues associated with HIV infections are issues no family desires to deal with—homosexuality, addiction, and incest.

The discovery of a relative's involvement with homosexual practices and relationships may devastate the family. However, most psychologists agree that the restrictive discipline of dysfunctional family background and underdeveloped psychosexual self-image could have led to these blatant homosexual activities—activities which draw the young person deeper and deeper into this addictive life style. Families of AIDS victims may react with guilt, anger, and a desire to separate further from their errant members. They may blame the young person's friends who were involved with sexual experimentation.

When the news of HIV has been received, the emotional reactions are amplified. A family member might think he or she is not only responsible for the homosexual family member's sexual errancy, but now for his or her early death as well.[7] The emancipation of the young homosexual will also hamper efforts for forgiveness and restoration of previous relationships.

Addictions are difficult for any family to handle, no matter if they are related to illicit drugs, alcohol, or sex. Ironically, family structure may facilitate the addiction; attempts to identify or treat the addicted member are often fraught with counterproductive behaviors by family members.[8] The characteristics seen in these addictive families include alcohol abuse, eating disorders, drug addiction, and other more acceptable compulsive behaviors like workaholism. These families are often physically, sexually, and emotionally abusive and neglectful, demonstrating a chaotic structure where family members' emotional needs are neither recognized or met.[9]

The complicating news of a fatal infection because of drug addiction may further ingrain the dysfunctional needs instead of exposing them for treatment and correction. The depth of dysfunction within the family can only be uncovered with in-depth counseling and a high degree of cooperation, neither of which is likely.

Sexual addictions, such as uncontrollable use of pornographic magazines, videos, use of prostitutes, or adulterous relationships also present difficult problems for family resolution. Approaching these problems with a full-scale, double-barrel approach is almost always necessary if resolution is to occur. Uncontrollable addiction may require intensive inpatient therapy as well as long-term accountability and counseling. HIV may further hamper any counseling efforts for reconciliation and family support.

Incest, the most serious form of sexual addiction and abuse, presents even greater complications to the counselor who is sorting through the maze of emotions, interactions, and relationships. When sexual abuse of the children is suspected, separate discussions with family members should be attempted and a confidence established. Once they reach twelve to fifteen years of age, young people become independent enough to seek help and protection from an abusing father. The mother must not be included in the confidential discussions with these children, because she is often a consenting party to the sexual abuse, even though she fervently denies its existence. Seeking the help of a child protective services agency or other social services

173

network is wise as soon as you suspect sexual abuse. Protective services will be the best source of information as how to proceed depending upon the laws in your state or province. From a legal standpoint, notification of the proper authorities is prudent protection for the counselor. In addition, it acts as protection for the family being helped. The sooner the family is confronted with the problem, the sooner it will begin the long, arduous healing process.

Everett

Everett's parents could not have been more supportive. They were interested in helping him cope with his hemophilia; and when they found out after Everett's screening blood test that he was HIV positive, they purposed to foster good health and a positive attitude during the time their twelve-year-old son had left.

Information collecting became their hobby. Each day they scanned three newspapers, looking for new information about medications and treatments for HIV. The best books that could be found were read and cataloged for future reference. Everett was placed on a strict "Daniel-like" diet, inspired by Daniel 1:12, that was high in vitamin C and other anti-oxidant vitamins, and included fish high in omega-3 fatty acids. An exercise program was devised with a bicycle because it was less jarring to the joints and less likely to cause any bleeding. He was home schooled to keep him away from common respiratory illnesses.

Fortunately, AZT was beginning to be offered on a trial basis for children, then, and his age, twelve, made him eligible for one arm of a research study. The physician checked him every other month and drew blood to check on his white blood cell counts and possible problems with the medication.

No changes were detected for more than two years. Then the medication started to fail and Everett ended up in the hospital with meningitis and oral candidiasis. Both of Everett's parents felt as if they had failed him. Guilt kept them away from the hospital and for several days only an aunt went by to see him. Everett soon became so sick that the physician called and told his parents that he was dying. "You need to be here!" he said emphatically.

With constant tears, a level of depression that made them feel ill, and great fear that Everett would "hate" them, they made their way to the sixth floor pediatrics area. Their level of trust had been so great in the vitamins, the diet, the exercise, the isolation, the physicians, and the medication that the failure caused an explosive, guilt-ridden grief reaction they were unprepared for. Their control over the disease was gone. And now they risked losing Everett as well.

Everett showed no anger. He did more than any counselor could when he told them, "The disease just got worse. If I make it through this, we'll just try harder."

He did make it through, but his parents fell back into the same compulsive patterns they had used before to shield themselves from having to deal with the grief. A second hospitalization again brought an almost hysterical reaction by the parents. The hospital chaplain talked with them about whom to trust, how to trust, and when to trust. They are still compulsive about Everett's care, but have been talking with the chaplain almost every week.

SUPPORTING THE SUPPORTIVE FAMILY

Supportive families come in all shapes and sizes. Families like Everett's are very good at meeting the physical needs associated with a long-term illness. They had to be to deal with the hemophilia. But their compulsive attitudes toward hemophilia and AIDS took the place of the grief process that needed to be started. Since they subconsciously refused to deal with the possibility of losing him, the reaction phase of their grief was delayed, deeper and more prolonged than most. Counselors will see many families who will be better at taking care of physical needs than the emotional needs of themselves or the AIDS patient.

Other families will be less able to meet the physical needs, because of time constraints, jobs, or other commitments than they are able to meet the emotional needs. In these cases counselors need to solicit the help of a social worker or someone who can arrange for home nursing, hospice volunteers, or other more medically oriented aid for the patient. Today's busy society and the pressure it creates infringe on the physical time commitments of parents, forcing them to use service agencies as often as possible.

Some of the families we will counsel will have some or most of the skills needed to care for their AIDS patients during the terminal months. The skills they do not have can be taught or obtained through local health-care agencies or the local hospital. But only a few family members will have the emotional tools needed to deal with their grief. Prior experience with a disease or with another family member who has died can add to their level of preparation. The stronger their faith, the more strength they will have available for grieving.

Our goal as counselors should be training families to deal with these emotional reactions so they can eventually help the patient through his or her own emotional reactions as death nears. Any way we can encourage the patient and his or her family to seek God's help during this time will add greatly to their ability to accept God's will in the final days. We can use this opportunity to disciple them spiritually during these counseling sessions. Underscoring the scriptural principles of suffering demonstrates the inseparability of the spiritual from the emotional. That discipling must be deeper than just praying with them, or reading a few scriptures, but encouraging them to study together, pray as a family for all the members' comfort, and to seek strength from their church congregation, friends, and pastor. Sadly, in a time of crisis, many family members drop their spiritual guard and "flee" from the church or their spiritual friends.

Dealing with their emotional reactions toward the illness and toward the dying family member not only brings comfort to the family members, but also makes them more supportive toward the one who needs their emotional help so desperately. Guiding them through the normal emotional reactions toward acceptance means identifying the types of defenses used, supporting their need to grieve, gently returning them to the reality of the illness, and encouraging them to pray for healing but accepting death if this is God's design and plan. The needs of the dying member should be our greatest motivation.

CAPTURING THE DISTANT FAMILY

Because many HIV patients will be young adults living on their own, gaining support from the family may be a difficult task, especially if there is a large physical distance separating the adult child from his or her family. Our task should be to establish the best and most supportive lines of communication possible, considering the distance. Yet, other families will be in closer and even convenient proximity, but emotionally they will be in a distant galaxy. Their self-created emotional distance protects them from the painful reminder of AIDS or a related behavior.[10] These two types of families present a challenge for the counselor whose support of the patient can bring comfort, but not nearly as much as a family can bring.

The key to pulling physically distant family members closer is to find the one person whose relationship with the patient is closest and warmest. Usually our patient can easily identify that member for us. With the patient's permission, we can then approach that person to solicit his or her help. In our initial conversation with him or her, we can see what level of understanding he or she may have about AIDS and at what level of the grief process that person is. We may be the one called upon to give the bad news. Calling back to see how the person is doing within a day or two can then be an opportunity to counsel them through the reactions toward acceptance.

Our key relative then becomes our link with the distant family. As he or she accepts the circumstances, hopefully that relative can help by contacting other members of the family. Simply asking the other members to call, write a brief note, send flowers, or in some other way show support can cheer our ill patient. If the family can be organized in some way, such as sharing the costs of travel to come to visit the distant AIDS victim, then the domino effect through our key relative has become a reality. I have had dying patients and grieving family members who stated that a "visit" from family or friends was the most comforting and encouraging help for which they could have wished. Don't underestimate what this little bit of effort can mean for the dying patient.

The more difficult challenge involves the emotionally distant family. And though this type of emotional situation may be difficult to diagnose and treat, the emotional benefits are tremendous if the problem can be resolved.

As expected, the first step in trying to reconcile estranged family members is to find one who is willing to talk openly. The patient may know why the estrangement exists, and he or she may be most helpful in opening the door through seeking to apologize for any disappointment or problems caused within the family. If the patient is not able to communicate this message, we can act as an emissary on his or her behalf, bringing messages of apology to other members and telling them of the seriousness of the patient's illness.

When a door opens, be persistent in communications with that family member. Educate that member concerning the patient's life, describing how he or she became infected, and how the disease is taking its toll, while soliciting sympathy and help from that member. Often, minimal grief will be expressed because little emotional investment in the patient has been made. Our counseling at this point should concentrate more on the aspects of family reconciliation than on helping family members deal with grief.

After he discovered he was infected with HIV, the greatest joy for Jay, whose story has been mentioned throughout this book, was his reconciliation with his estranged father. My brief counsel for Jay seemingly worked well. "Just approach your father with the truth of how you contracted AIDS. Let God do the rest." Our prayers were answered. The year before Jay died, God granted him a greatly improved relationship with his father, who supported him emotionally up until his death.

DEALING WITH GRIEF

Grief, as expressed by family members, follows the same line of emotional reactions as the patient's, including acceptance and maturation. In fact, most of the studies of these emotional reactions were not accomplished on dying patients, but on the spouses of those who had died from an illness or accident. The classic models of grief, as well as the Unified Theory of Grief, however, appear to fit both patient and family.[11] Further study and refinement of patients' reactions just prior to death still need to be accomplished, as do studies of the grief process and how it is affected by AIDS.[12]

The grief that families feel toward an AIDS-infected member may be different from other terminal illnesses. The stigma of

AIDS and the desire of family members to be distanced from the disease makes grieving more difficult. Some members will attempt to hide their grief at all costs, fearing someone will ask them "why are you upset?" Turning these emotions inward can only cause more suffering for the individual. It also prolongs the emotional phase of grieving, possibly to the point that it will become pathological.

Acceptance of the disease will also be more difficult. How could someone in their family become infected, and even die, from a disease of perversion or addiction? How could God be so unfair to allow this "curse" to be placed within their family? Why couldn't he or she die of some other, less embarrassing, disease? Though these comments seem rather cold and callous, we are likely to hear them many more times than we wish.[13]

Education is the only known cure for halting this type of emotional discrimination and keeping it from becoming even more widespread. We must realize that a significant amount of fear still exists about casual-contact spread of AIDS. The families of our patients may demonstrate these fears.[14] If the family appears to understand the disease, has accepted its reality on an emotional level, but still appears reluctant to physically or emotionally support the patient, fear of casual-contact spread should be suspected. Beyond talking with family members about their fears, we can be an example by touching, talking with, and hugging the patient. Our caring example can reduce the family members' anxieties and encourage them to show more support.

PARENTS OF AIDS CHILDREN

The tragic reality of AIDS in children is the most devastating part of this epidemic. For families, there is no sadder loss than the death of a child. Many of the youngest and most innocent are infected prior to birth and usually die before their fifth birthday. In New York City, of every sixty-one children born, one child is already HIV positive.

"We have lost a generation of hemophiliac children," one hematologist once told me when he quoted the disturbing reality of a 92 percent infection rate among hemophiliacs.[15]

Parents of hemophiliac children usually have some emotional preparation for AIDS because they have been dealing with a potentially fatal disorder since its discovery. But their investment in the care of their child has been greater than those who have reared healthy children. In addition, they must also deal with the guilt of knowing one of their "genes" was responsible for both the hemophilia, and its treatment, which resulted in AIDS. More than one child in their family may have hemophilia, doubling the risk and the grief.

The best strategies for counseling a family with hemophilia includes anticipatory counseling for the inevitable grief that will occur, as well as frank discussions with the parents about putting aside their guilt. Parents of a diabetic child usually do not dwell on their roles in contributing a defective gene to their son or daughter. Some do feel guilt, but not to the extent that many parents of a hemophiliac child feel it. Dealing with this guilt will give the most therapeutic relief for these parents. Dealing with the other emotional reactions, relationships, and communication difficulties will bolster the emotional support parents can give their dying child.

When a newborn baby is infected, the mother is also infected. Because the medications to treat AIDS and prolong life were first available for adults, many of these children die before their mothers. The mother must then deal emotionally with her own death, as well as the child's, and families must deal with the loss of two members, possibly three if the father is also infected. The depth and severity of grief within these families will be tremendous. Our involvement will need to be greater from a time standpoint, and more intense from an emotional standpoint.

Whenever the task is overwhelming, our reaction may be to throw up our hands and retreat. We must resist that natural reaction if at all possible and enlist the help of as many others as can be recruited to help these doubly infected families. Hospice organizations, social agencies, social workers, church members, pastors, friends, or more distant family members, all are needed if we hope to give these families adequate support during their most difficult moments.

GROUPS AND MINISTRIES

The emotional needs of families with AIDS will vary greatly. Each has needs that can be met through support groups and ministries that deal specifically with their emotional trauma. For example, there are support groups for parents of homosexual AIDS victims that deal with the problems of homosexual activities and with AIDS. Most of these groups consist of those who do not hold the scriptural view of homosexual addiction and thus try to support parents with "it's-OK-to-be-gay" rhetoric. Though judgment should not be a part of these support groups, a more biblical view of the causes and treatment of homosexual "orientation" would be more therapeutic and more guilt relieving.

Other support groups exist for all the major genres of AIDS infection: drug addicts, and parents of drug addicts, heterosexual groups, hemophiliac groups, and parents of children with AIDS. These groups are usually found in metropolitan areas. But national networks are forming to help meet the emotional needs of this varied group of families through sharing of experiences, networking, and up-to-date information.

PART THREE

MINISTERING TO THOSE
IN NEED

CHAPTER ELEVEN

THE CHURCH'S ROLE IN AIDS

From my usual Sunday morning seat in the church choir, I have an excellent view of the future of AIDS. Our sanctuary holds about four thousand people, and scattered through the nursery, children's, and young-adult classrooms are about four thousand more. Many of the people I see in the sanctuary are also my patients. Some of the young people have been seen for physicals, others for typical childhood and adult health problems, and a few of the senior members of the congregation have come for problems ranging from high blood pressure to cancer. I know many of them well, and love them all dearly.

This seems an unlikely group to be associated with AIDS. But AIDS is an epidemic, and already it has touched even Christian congregations. In the United States, 1 out of every 75 men in the United states is infected with HIV.[1] Some estimates suggest more are infected, approximately 3.5 million persons, or 1.4 percent of the total population.[2] By 1995, almost 3 percent could be infected, a total of 9 million persons.[3] I shudder to think that as many as 112 people sitting in church classes and sanctuary could be infected with HIV. Because we reside in a small, mostly rural city, the number may be half, or even less than half, maybe 20 to 30 people. But AIDS has already touched this congregation. Jay, whose infection came from the AIDS-contaminated injection in Haiti, was a Watchcare member of our church—officially a member of another church, but affiliated with this congregation while he attended college in our city. Only 3 people in the congregation knew that he had AIDS when he died.

Where and who are the others? Are they partaking in risky sexual behaviors within the church family? As mentioned earlier, well-documented studies of Christian youth tell us that 60 percent or more are sexually active prior to marriage.[4] We don't know how many have used IV drugs, but secular studies have estimated a range between 1 and 3 percent of the population.[5] If there are AIDS-infected mothers in this congregation, then their babies have a chance of being infected as well.

Are we really insulated from AIDS in our church sanctuaries? Do the steeple and the four church walls offer protection from this epidemic? If the number of AIDS cases is increasing at such a rapid rate, how many church members will be infected ten years from now? And once an AIDS victim realizes his or her need for a Savior, won't he or she be seeking a church home in which to worship?

This book has included descriptions of AIDS victims who were already Christians or who became Christians as a result of their disease. Yes, Christians have become infected and have died from AIDS. Their testimonies have been utilized here because similar clients who will use pastoral and professional counseling will be seeking our expertise for the spiritual insight we can give to this problem.

The spiritual condition of the millions who are HIV positive is unknown. But God can use this epidemic to commence a great spiritual awakening among those who are infected with HIV and also their families.[6] Similarly, God used disease plagues in Old Testament days to awaken the hardened hearts of the Hebrew children, bringing about a widespread spiritual recommitment.[7] Because we believe that God's timing is always perfect and his methods are always effective, it appears now that our entire culture, including the church, may be on the verge of spiritual awakening and renewal. The need for revival could not be greater.

A revealing series of events has shocked those who follow modern media-based Christianity. A number of very prominent Christian evangelists and businessmen have succumbed to personal temptation in their lives, even to the point of involvement with serious sexual addictions. After these evangelists' fall from power became daily news, more churches lost their leadership to the same immorality.

We must deal with the immorality within the church immediately or else we will forfeit many of our young people to the ravages of sexual addiction, drug usage, and AIDS. Previous efforts to call sin sin have fallen on deaf ears—ears that are constantly hearing about the pleasure of those sins through print and video media. The church must develop a clear, concise, and far-reaching method of retrieving these young adults before they are lost to the siren song of this promiscuous modern culture. We must restore confidence in the message we preach. Judgmental messages may be accurate, but these messages are competing on the free market of the American mind and will be turned off before they are received. Instead, a tactful, loving, and firm message must be proclaimed clearly, boldly, intelligently, and immediately. There is too much at stake to do otherwise!

The church has an important role to play in protecting those who are listening to its message, to those who will seek spiritual guidance through salvation, and to those outside the church who need the gospel. The ministry potential for reaching the millions of susceptible young people is immense. Our efforts should focus on preventing infections through the spiritual message of unconditional acceptance while we attempt to rescue those who are already infected.

CHURCH-WIDE EDUCATION

The crisp, cool air of a New England fall day filled the air. I had been asked to give a church-wide seminar on the scientific and biblical aspects of AIDS. Since this church was near a larger city, AIDS was an already known and accepted fact. But many of the church members felt strongly that ministering to AIDS victims should be accomplished outside of the church; some evangelical preachers had suggested this course as the only safe option. So I was honored to see almost half of the church attend on that beautiful Saturday morning; they were there because they needed and wanted to know about AIDS.

A few weeks later, in a call from the pastor I received good news about a young lady I had met at the seminar. She had been addicted to IV drugs and was infected with HIV. Later, she professed Christ as her Savior and, at the time of the seminar, had been trying to find a church. She had wanted to be honest with the church before she joined, but she had met with resistance from some of the leaders. A church-wide vote after the AIDS seminar voted Linda, and any other AIDS victim, the right and privilege of attending church and all functions. It was a bold and correct decision that the church members made for themselves. The time was ripe for this congregation to minister to HIV-infected persons in their community.

Education is the key to putting unwarranted fears and discriminatory attitudes out of our minds. The pastor may not feel qualified to speak on the scientific aspects of AIDS with any degree of expertise. And local physicians may not have the time to help with specific AIDS information for congregations or ministries. But it *must* be accomplished, and the sooner the better.

A good way to start is by assigning some of the church leaders to put together a church-wide seminar about HIV which could include medical professionals, counseling professionals, and a strong spiritual message to adult and youth classes. The committee format should make sure than any objectionable information is screened and changed to a more acceptable form. If the church schedules an entire day or half-day for the subject, people are bound to understand its importance.

An excellent study guide on the approach to and the education of church members is now available for churches. Produced by MAP International and Americans for a Sound AIDS/HIV Policy, it contains information ranging from setting up educational seminars all the way down to suggested questions to ask participants.[8] A number of experts in the field, such as Dr. Robert Redfield, chief of AIDS research at the National Institutes of Health, as well as pastors, health educators, and physicians, including myself, were invited by these groups to participate and to share our knowledge and experience in preparing this study guide.

One local Virginia church is tackling the AIDS problem in a different but equally responsible and helpful way. The pastor and deacons have given permission to the youth director to sponsor discussions about sexuality and AIDS as part of the regular Sunday school curriculum.[9] This church is also holding special rallies and weekend retreats to concentrate on these subjects. It has made sexuality, drugs, and AIDS a spiritual priority as a means of protecting its young people from common adolescent mistakes. Not surprisingly, the youth group has greatly increased in size since the church decided to offer this material.

A dear friend of mine who teaches a similar Sunday school class at the college level has also had an overwhelming response to these subjects. He talks about dating, God-honoring relationships, and the scriptural principles for male-female relationships; and his classes are always overflowing.

Josh McDowell of Campus Crusade for Christ has spoken all over the country to Christian and secular university and high-school students. His upbeat and positive messages are always well accepted. But the one that draws overflowing crowds is his talk about "men and women." He takes a no-nonsense approach about premarital sexuality that is biblical in content—and extremely popular. Many of the materials he uses have been published and tapes of his lectures are also available.[10]

Whatever your church decides to do and whatever route you use—seminars, youth classes, videos and tapes—your church needs to make a decision to do something. Your help in convincing others that this important information should be given in more than family talks could help save many lives. Of course, family talks should also occur; parents should talk to their children and teach them the biblical view of sexuality. The church must be prepared to train parents and also to offer guidance to adolescents whose parents do not feel qualified to teach. If families and churches don't offer the Christian view, then there will be no voice except the promiscuous and beguiling voice giving the world's view of sexual pleasure without responsibility.

Organization and Training for an AIDS Ministry

If it is interested in an AIDS ministry, a church should begin by assessing the need within its own community. Is there a significant IV drug abuse problem? Is the church close to or within a large city? Is there a conclave of homosexuals within the community who are potentially infected? Is the need primarily educational, teaching young adults how to prevent the infection? How can a church study to see if these needs are present and how are they being addressed by other groups?

The county or city health department is the best place to start. Ask them how large the AIDS problem is in the area of the church and what kinds of programs they offer for patients or their families. The local hospital, the United Way agency, and possibly other service organizations may offer some programs or other help for AIDS victims as well. A few hours of making phone calls is usually sufficient to know how large the problem is and what is offered in your community.

Once the need is assessed, a proposal can be offered to the leaders of the church, with final approval by a general vote. If the only area of need is for education of the youth within the church, then offering to have some curriculum for the Sunday school department should be a useful solution. If there are counseling and "helper" needs, such as a need for visitation and volunteers to help with minor chores around the house of an AIDS victim, then training can be offered for this type of a lay counseling position. Any type of ministry, from a small educational ministry to the larger, fully funded drug-rehabilitation ministry is possible if the need is present and resources can be found to support the work. Your imagination is your limit in how you can help those with needs.

Training is a necessity for all those involved with an AIDS program, no matter what level or kind of ministry is offered. Teachers should be given the information to be taught well before an orientation meeting so they can properly review the material. Any concepts that are objectionable can be deleted or changed at that meeting to reduce complaints. Any questions can be answered by a medical expert who can be present at the meeting. Sensitivity to families and students must be guarded to ensure the educational sessions are supported fully by the church.

The more complex the ministry, the more planning and training must be accomplished prior to getting a congregation involved. If members are planning a personal-outreach ministry, with lay people going into the homes of AIDS patients to be a friend, to help around the house, and to run errands for them, then these members need more specialized training, which can be provided by a nurse, health educator, or physician. This type of ministry presents no risk to participants unless they perform nursing tasks such as handling bedpans, blood, secretions, or changing bandages. Volunteers should not become involved with these tasks unless properly trained and properly protected (bandages on cuts, gloves to protect skin). If the church member desires to be more available and to give more "medical" care, then training in "universal precautions" can be given.[11]

Obviously, personnel for a medical-care or drug-rehabilitation ministry must have further training in very specialized areas. This may exclude many lay people from working full time at one of these ministries; but volunteers can help with a host of nonspecialized tasks, such as cleaning, construction, maintenance, and transportation.

People with AIDS have many needs that ordinary people can help meet. These personal ministries are an excellent way to offer care and open the door for the gospel.

PERSONAL MINISTRIES

Alberta

About twice a week, Alberta went to see Bruce, whom she had adopted as sort of surrogate grandson. He had been in the navy and had traveled extensively. While he was enlisted, he had become addicted to cocaine and had tried some injectable medication a few times at a party. At various ports of call, he also had been sexually active with dates and with one prostitute. Three years after his discharge, Bruce became ill with AIDS.

Alberta had met him at the local food store while he was still up and about. They lived in the same apartment complex. She felt a spiritual burden for him, and she kept praying for an opportunity to witness. By the time she mustered the strength to fix her special blueberry pie and her courage to take it to his apartment, a number of months had passed. She could tell something was wrong. Recurring infections, along with the damage to the brain and spinal cord, had sapped his strength. He was barely able to take care of himself around the apartment.

She came back the next week—and the next. Then she became a regular visitor, bringing food each time. Bruce opened up and talked about his family and himself, and Alberta was able to share the gospel with him a number of times during these visits.

Just think of the needs any infirm person might have: help with opening and reading the mail or reaching under the table to clean up a spill, a friend who will just sit and listen, a repairman for minor problems that happen in any home, reading a book, running errands, writing out checks, or any other simple or complex task. A weekly visit and talk gives a shut-in encouragement for the lonely times. Fixing a few hot meals a week for AIDS victims who cannot handle pots and pans because of numbness will make their diet fuller and more nutritious.

There is no end to the types of help you can give. But you also have to find someone who needs your help.

The Lord may just happen to lead you to that AIDS patient, just as he led Alberta to Bruce. Letting others in your congregation know that you are interested in helping an AIDS patient might produce a name or a suggestion. As I was standing near the nursery one Sunday evening, a woman told me, "If you know of an AIDS baby that needs someone, let me know. I believe the Lord is calling me to mother a homeless AIDS child." Besides talking to your physician and leaving your name and number with him or her, you could call the local health department or hospital and volunteer yourself to be an AIDS "buddy."

"Buddy" Ministries

Many programs were developed by members of the gay community to give each other support when AIDS became a personal realty. The "buddy" program, one of the more successful programs, has been introduced across the country to minister to the needs of people with AIDS. "Buddies" are volunteer friends who give of their time, of themselves, and sometimes of their substance to help and support AIDS victims. The jobs they perform are immensely important—yet very easy. For example, they wait with their buddies in the physicians' offices, visit them in the hospital, or run out to fetch them an occasional soft drink.

The training that is offered varies, as does the program. Many programs are patterned after those in the gay community and may include "desensitization" to the homosexual life-style. No matter how strongly we feel about promiscuous sexuality, Christ has called us to love the sinner in an unconditional way. Without showing his unconditional love, we won't be given the opportunity to share his gospel.

Who becomes the buddies for these AIDS patients? Just about anyone can. Married or single, young or old, white-collar or blue-collar, everyone can learn to minister to simple needs that give us the opportunity to share what God means to us. But remember that any patients who discern that your major interest in them is to "get em' for God" will quickly withdraw from the relationship and ask for another buddy. Instead, we can win them as we show them our love.

A buddy builds a caring relationship with another, needy, human being. The time, unfortunately, to build this relationship is limited by the course of the disease. Immersing oneself in this type of "all-giving" relationship benefits the giver as much if not more than the AIDS patient. Listen to the testimony of someone involved in a buddy program:

What types of things are gained? The joy on the face of your "buddy" as you throw a birthday party for him, likely to be his last. The simple pleasure of letting your "buddy" tell his mother-in-law jokes, and laughing whether they were humorous or not. The happiness in the face of your

193

new friend because you shared the most precious thing you have—yourself.[12]

HOSPICE MINISTRIES

Most people don't quite know what a "hospice" program is. Diane didn't understand much about it until a friend urged her to go to a meeting and volunteer to help. As a premedical student, she agreed in order to gain some medical experience.

After her training she was assigned to an older gentleman who had cancer of the pancreas. She felt very uncomfortable at first, believing that her supportive role would be difficult because of the pain involved. The visions she had of her patient were of an old, dying man, yelling for his paper, his water, his slippers, and his urinal. To her pleasant surprise, he was awake and alert. He just wanted someone to talk with him while his family worked most of the day. They quickly found some common interests, such as wildflowers and hiking.

The older gentleman died quietly in his sleep one evening. Diane was assured that his spiritual commitment was solid. She had read to him before he went to sleep that night. As we talked about her experience, she said, "I just can't see why more Christians don't volunteer to help."

Hospice programs are not designed to be "Christian" in orientation, but simply to help those who are terminally ill to die at home, with comfort and with dignity. Many facilities have been initiated, built, and run by Christian groups, as were the original hospice programs.[13] Now, hospice programs take on many shapes and sizes, ranging from local programs that send volunteers to homes, to large inpatient facilities. The escalating death rate from AIDS has created a mushrooming need for more trained staff members, trained volunteers, and for facilities and equipment to care for these patients. Unless the epidemic is slowed through education and medications, the need for humane "death" care will constantly be greater than the programs and facilities available.[14]

A family or individual could become involved in a tremendously difficult, but highly rewarding ministry called "home hospice care." These self-sacrificing people open their homes, offering shelter, food, and care for dying AIDS patients.

A widow or single person could rent a room or basement apartment, and offer to give care as the AIDS patient had needs. Special training could be provided to educate care givers how to handle certain situations or specific health problems.

The difficulties of "home hospice care" for a terminally ill person must be anticipated and well thought through. Here are some questions that should be asked in anticipation of becoming involved with this type of ministry. Would you mind if someone died in your home? If your family decided to take on this ministry, who would be responsible for what, and where would family members be trained? If the relationship caused too much grief for the host or the patient, how would the AIDS patient be asked to leave and where would he or she go? Could the individual or family find others within their congregation who would also want to lend a hand?

> A new command I give you: Love one another. As I have loved you, so you must love one another. By this all men will know that you are my disciples, if you love one another. (John 13:34–35)

How much do we really love our neighbors, our fellow believers, our own family members? Most families today would not even open their home to a dying mother or father, let alone an AIDS victim from their church or from the local health department. Opening one's home to care for someone with tremendous personal and physical problems can be very difficult for a family or individual. I can tell you this from personal experience. But shouldn't we be willing to sacrifice some comfort for the opportunity to witness to others? The love that we show with our actions speaks much more loudly than words.

The monetary rewards for this type of ministry are nil, and the emotional rewards are few; but the spiritual rewards are so vast they cannot be counted.

"HARD-HEARTED" MINISTRIES

Because of their life styles, a few in our congregations will be granted safe passage and possible ministry into areas of our society where even the brave dare not go. Linda, a young

195

woman with AIDS, had a burden to go back into her drug culture, win her friends to the Lord, and wrestle them from their addictions. After Jerry became infected with AIDS, he was able to win some of his homosexual partners to the gospel; they listened to him, because he was one of them. Tom, an ex-drug addict before the threat of AIDS, now leads a church in his old stomping ground, in downtown Manhattan. The ministry God has given him, to pull drug addicts out of their enslaving habits, is known all over New York City. And the list goes on all across this country.

Men and women have been called to return to the wretched life styles they left at the time of their conversion to minister to their friends. Homosexual addicts would not trust a middle-aged pastor as much as they trust someone who has lived that life style. The same occurs in the drug culture, a close group which is even harder to penetrate and minister to. In those situations, former alcoholics are more believable and more trusted by those who are still using drugs. It is often God's plan to use those with softened hearts to reach those who are still "hard-hearted" toward his word.

LARGER CHURCH MINISTRIES

Probably you have heard most of the arguments concerning the pros and cons of large churches versus small churches. But when it comes to the potential for specialized ministries to groups who need extraordinary amounts of care, its usually the larger churches who have sufficient resources to meet the demand. Many of these specialized ministries, such as alcohol rehabilitation, food for the needy, pregnancy care for unwed mothers, camping ministries, nursing homes, retirement homes, television ministries, colleges, and Christian schools, could only have come about through the dedication and hard work of a large congregation to supply the prayer and financial support.

The epidemic of AIDS brings to mind other areas of ministry that large churches could tackle. These include drug rehabilitation, homosexual ministries, sexual-addiction counseling, and possibly hospice homes where terminal AIDS patients and others with terminal illnesses could be cared for. Any program that includes medical care will be expensive because it needs to provide the expertise, materials, and training. But many of the medical costs can be reimbursed through government funding such as Medicaid for those patients who qualify.

Drug Rehabilitation Ministries

Despite the usual requirement of substantial resources, the best example of a drug rehabilitation ministry that I can give is a program that was not started by an extremely large or affluent church. Instead, it began in the heart of Tom, the ex-drug addict mentioned earlier, whom the Lord brought out of that life style and placed at the helm of an inner-city church. His New York City ministry primarily cares for those addicted to intravenous drugs, and has expanded to care for those who have AIDS because of their addiction.

The trip from Manhattan Bible Church to its drug rehabilitation "farm" outside the city takes about an hour and a half. "Addicts have to be removed from their environment," said pastor Tom, explaining one of the most important concepts in treating serious addictions. After the initial drying-out period, the ex-addicts become involved in a regimented program of spiritual time, work, exercise, and recreation, followed by more work, and more spiritual time. Those who are HIV positive are treated no differently than those who are not. All participants are given basic information about AIDS, how to be tested, what a positive test means, and how to avoid AIDS in the future. The program has an excellent success rate, the greatest success coming from those who have made the greatest spiritual commitment.

Funding for the program is handled through private donations, donations from sister churches, and offerings at Manhattan Bible Church, which has become the church home for many of these rehabilitated addicts.

Sexual Addiction Ministries

The catastrophic revelations about uses of prostitutes, church secretaries, and even homosexual relationships of famous Christian television personalities brought to light a deep problem within today's churches.

How could this happen? Does the power offered to these church leaders tempt them beyond that which they are able to resist? Or has the sexual ethic of the world slowly and decisively dissected its way into the hearts and minds of many in the church's pews and pulpits, including the immature and potentially promiscuous adolescents in our youth groups? Perhaps both are painfully true. But who is willing to talk about the problem, work with those afflicted, or even set up a confidential way for these addicts to get help?

The best place for Christians to get counseling or treatment for their sexual addictions is in the midst of other, usually distant churches. The need for removing the addicts from their "environment" is important, because in their new setting, they are removed from the relationships that are tempting them, from the stores that are feeding them, and from the congregations where the rumors and innuendoes are slowly destroying the addicts and their families. Pastors or counselors who are familiar with treatment programs for alcohol- and drug-abuse could sponsor a limited program for those with sexual addiction, allowing these people a place to overcome their problems before AIDS becomes a permanent part of their lives.

Homosexual Ministries

Churches in some of the larger metropolitan cities where the homosexual culture flourishes have initiated various outreach programs to these persons. Most help build one-on-one relationships between homosexual and "helpers," and offering assistance through counseling, confidential HIV testing, and ministries to homosexual AIDS patients in the hospital wards. The most successful programs are run by former homosexuals who speak directly to the needs of these people from a spiritual and emotional standpoint.[15] From their testimonies of conversion and sexual reorientation, these ex-homosexual Christians have been the most effective at penetrating the tough emotional shell meant to protect gay persons from the scorn of our culture.

MEDICAL CARE OPTIONS FOR CHURCHES

Should churches provide medical care, medications, nursing care, hospice care, nursing home, or hospital care for AIDS patients? Some are doing this now, and many others will join with them in the future.

Free clinics, sponsored by consortia of churches in many small to large cities, offer medical care, nursing care, dental care, counseling, and medications without charge to the poor and indigent in their neighborhoods. A percentage of these patients will be HIV positive by virtue of their drug addictions or sexual promiscuity. This may be the most common place for AIDS care to be given in the next century because HIV positivity is growing much faster in cities than in the rural areas.

Any church that owns or could buy or rent an old house, and which can organize medical and nursing care along with general volunteers, can run a group home for AIDS patients. How does a church plan such a ministry? The number of AIDS patients that have no place else to go must first be assessed. Then, the types of patients, the degree of illness, and the amount of medical care should be ascertained as part of the planning. The necessity for state approval or licensing should be ascertained early in the process. Once the house has been purchased and appropriately refurbished, then volunteers can be organized to provide necessary services such as cleaning, becoming a "buddy," fixing meals, giving rides to physicians' offices, or whatever else is needed. A thorough training program is essential as you start this ministry, and as new volunteers are recruited.

Here is an interesting concept of perpetual care: In an "AIDS home," less-ill AIDS patients can be called upon to give care to more seriously ill or terminally AIDS patients. This can be accomplished by housing together both AIDS patients who have longer to live and also those who are closer to death. The healthier patients care for the sicker patients. The emotional support offered to the "healthier" patients must be excellent. Constant surveillance is needed to prevent rapid emotional deterioration, and the advent of serious depression or suicide.[16] The spiritual ministry, sharing the gospel with the sick and terminally ill, should always be the central purpose and theme in any program of the church.

To Love the Unlovely

Since my spiritual conversion in 1973, I have always had a fascination with the medical aspects of Scripture, especially how our Lord treated those who suffered with the various diseases of his day. It seems that Christ's ministry to those with leprosy, a feared and stigmatized disease, is mentioned more than any other disease or disorder. Is there a reason for this?

Two thoughts come to mind.

Few diseases were as disfiguring as this dreaded disease, leprosy. The scarring around the nose and eyes, the loss of fingers, toes, feet, and hands, the white patches of skin splotched in the middle of an olive or tan complexion, made the disease odious to bystanders, neighbors, and even family members. Society had no choice but to protect itself from this ugly blight that afflicted some of its members. The unlovely were banished to colonies where they would suffer and die with other "sinners."

How did the disease cause this disfigurement and destruction? Simply by destroying the victims' ability to feel pain. Burns, cuts, and simple infections—little problems that would have been easily discovered and cared for by persons with normal sensations—would go unnoticed by the leprosy victim. Eventually, after more injury or infection, the problems then became so severe that fingers, hands, or even arms could be lost. Without the sensation of pain, the lepers would continue to damage and destroy parts of their own anatomy.

The ministry of Jesus Christ showed no partiality. It didn't matter how disfigured, how unlovely, how scarred the lepers were. Jesus ministered to any and all who desired his touch. He ministered to their physical pain, their emotional suffering, and their spiritual needs. He showed us by his example that even the unlovely leper was to be included in his ministry to the multitudes. His example of ministering to all races, creeds, nations, and diseases is clear. If we desire to obey his commands, we must also be willing and obedient to minister to all types of people.

AIDS is the leprosy of the twentieth century, the most feared disease of our day. It also leads to disfiguring splotches of the skin, Kaposi's sarcomas. The organism that causes HIV slowly destroys its target tissues, specifically the T-lymphocytes and nerve tissues. The patient is afflicted with fevers, swollen lymph nodes, and often loses stamina and weight. It is remarkable how similar AIDS is to leprosy.

It also appears that the fear of AIDS today is similar to the fear of leprosy felt by those living in Jesus' day. Just as leprosy deadens the sensations of the nerves, so the fear of AIDS has deadened the sensitivity of the heart, creating an unfeeling numbness toward those with AIDS. Like the masses of people in the time of Christ, many today desire to separate AIDS victims as far away as possible, placing them in "colonies" to suffer with others of like "sin."

I pray that God will impress upon our hearts the reason he placed leprosy above other diseases, and why his ministry to the lepers was so prominent. May Christ's ministry of loving the unlovely lepers be an example for each of us as we minister to the unlovely victims of AIDS.

A SPIRITUAL VISION OF
OUR FUTURE

The year is 2005.

Many excellent advances have been made in the diagnosis and treatment of the condition once named **AIDS**, now simply called **HIV** disease. A number of vaccines are on the market that use the stable proteins in the viral capsid or covering. Most of these vaccines have a success rate of 80 to 90 percent. But each year the group of viruses that cause **HIV** disease changes enough that a new formulation of the older vaccines is necessary to maintain protection. Most people who are actively exposed to **HIV** are being revaccinated every six months.

The advances in the ways we treat **HIV** are also amazing.

Some of the newer, long-acting topical contraceptives, such as the one-way-permeable cervical cap, and some of the oral hormonal and spermicidal contraceptive are also effective in preventing HIV absorption at the time of intercourse. Of course, these contraceptives, vaccines, and protections from HIV are costly and are not yet available in the Third World.

The effects of educational efforts began to bear fruit in the mid-1990s, slowing, but not eradicating, the rate of new infections of HIV—and all sorts of other venereal diseases. The rate of new infections in the 1990s was exponential; each year the number of cases doubled, until this slowed to a linear rise in the number of infections. We are now, with all our new technology, just starting to decrease the number of new infections that occur each year, which is easily ten million worldwide.

Behavioral scientists report seeing changes since the 1990s in many areas related to HIV disease. Their reports suggest that there are many fewer homosexuals, by percentage of population, than there were in the 1970s to 1990s. HIV has taken a heavy toll on their numbers, and on their ability to recruit more members into their pleasure-oriented, urban life style. It is far less attractive to be "gay" now than it was in the last century. Marriages are now more stable, divorces for sexual reasons much less common. Premarital intercourse has diminished through peer-pressure programs, such as "Say No to Sex," to less than 30 percent. However, the numbers are beginning to rise again with the advent of these newer contraceptive technologies that protect against HIV.

The one sociological change that has been remarkable, and scientists have been totally unable to explain, is the phenomenal growth of those adhering to the evangelical religious groups. An explosion of interest in spiritual things has resulted in what many Christians call a "national revival." Everywhere there are lapel pins, bumper stickers, Bibles, and other Christian paraphernalia proclaiming Christ as Savior and Lord. The highly conservative shift in the political, economic, and social climate has been attributed solely to the spiritual renaissance that occurred in the late 1990s and into this century. Some say it "makes Ronald Reagan look like a liberal." Many blame the epidemic of **HIV** disease as the major reason for people "turning to God" in such an explosive manner.

HIV disease, its treatment, diagnosis, and prevention have changed dramatically since the early 1990s. But HIV disease has permanently changed the United States by inaugurating the "spiritual awakening of the twenty-first century."

APPENDIX 1

REFERENCES

The following is a list of ministries, groups, books, pamphlets, videos, and tapes that discuss various aspects of AIDS/HIV. The author and publisher offer this list for the reader who needs further resources or information. We do not, however, agree with all of the information offered by these groups or within these references.

We would like to acknowledge the help of Shepherd and Anita Smith, founders and coordinators of Americans for a Sound AIDS/HIV Policy, for their contribution in compiling the list of ministries, groups, and materials. Their dedication and hard work in helping to educate our citizens, potentially preventing thousands of cases of AIDS, has been an inspiration to each of us ministering to those with HIV.

National Ministries and Groups

Americans for a Sound AIDS/HIV Policy
P.O. Box 17433
Washington, D.C. 20041
703/471–7350

AIDS Crisis & Christians Today (ACCT)
P.O. Box 24647
Nashville, Tennessee 37202–4647
615/371–1616

LIGHT Associates, Inc.
Christian Professional Counseling and Medical Services
2900 Old Forest Road
Lynchburg, Virginia 25403
804/384–1581

AIDS Information Ministries
P.O. Box 136116
Fort Worth, Texas 76136
817/237–0230

AIDS Action Council
729 Eighth Street, SE, Suite 200
Washington, D.C. 20003
202/547–3101

National AIDS Network
1012 14th Street, NW, Suite 601
Washington, D.C. 20005
202/347–0390

Mothers of AIDS Patients
P.O. Box 3132
San Diego, California 92103
619/293–3985

Books about HIV and the Church

Albers, Gregg, M.D. *Plague in Our Midst: Sexuality, AIDS, and the Christian Family.* Lafayette, La.: Huntington House, 1988. 174 pages.

Amos, William. *When AIDS Comes to the Church.* Philadelphia: Westminster Press, 1988. 132 pages.

The Church's Response to the Challenge of AIDS/HIV: A Guideline for Education and Policy Development, published by Americans for a Sound AIDS/HIV Policy, MAP International, P.O. Box 17433, Washington, D.C., 20041, 1990. 60 pages.

Dixon, Patrick, M.D. *The Whole Truth about AIDS.* Nashville: Thomas Nelson Publishers, 1989. 246 pages.

Hoffman, Wendell, M.D., and Stanley Grenz, Th.D. *AIDS: Ministry in the Midst of an Epidemic.* Grand Rapids, Mich.: Baker Book House, 1990. 304 pages.

Malloy, Michael, *Am I My Brother's Keeper? The AIDS Crisis and the Church.* Kansas City, Mo.: Beacon Hill Press, 1990.

Perry, Shirleen. *In Sickness and in Health: A Story of Love in the Shadow of AIDS.* Downers Grove, Ill.: InterVarsity Press, 1989. 201 pages.

Shelp, Earl, and Ronald Sunderland. *AIDS and the Church.* Philadelphia: Westminster Press, Philadelphia, 1987. 154 pages.

Smith, Shepherd, and Anita Moreland Smith. *Christians in the Age of AIDS: How We Can be Good Samaritans Responding to the AIDS Crisis?* Wheaton, Ill.: Victor Books. 1990.

White, Margarite, M.D. *AIDS and the Positive Alternatives.* Grand Rapids, Mich.: Zondervan Publishing House, 1988. 118 pages.

Wood, Glenn, M.D., and John Dietrich, M.D. *The AIDS Epidemic: Balancing Compassion and Justice.* Portland, Ore.: Multnomah, 1990. 380 pages.

Books about HIV and Sexuality

Albers, Gregg, M.D. *Plague in Our Midst: Sexuality, AIDS, and the Christian Family.* Lafayette, La.: Huntington House, 1988. 174 pages.

Alcorn, Randy. *Christians in the Wake of the Sexual Revolution: Recovering Our Sexual Sanity,* Portland, Ore.: Multnomah Press, 1985. 314 pages.

Concordia Sex Education Series. Six books presenting a Christian perspective on human sexuality for children of all ages. Concordia Publishing House, Saint Louis, Mo.

Doney, Malcolm, and Meryl Doney. *Who Made Me?* Grand Rapids, Mich.: Zondervan Publishing House, 1987. 138 pages.

Gordon and Gordon. *Raising a Child Conservatively in a Sexually Permissive World.* New York: Simon and Schuster, 1986. 224 pages.

Ketterman, G. *How to Teach Your Child about Sex.* Old Tappan, N.J.: Fleming H. Revell Co., 1981.

Masters, William, Virginia Johnson, and R. Kolodny. *Crisis: Heterosexual Behavior in the Age of AIDS,* New York: Grove Press, 1988. 234 pages.

Penner, Clifford, and Joyce Penner. *A Gift for All Ages.* Waco, Tex.: Word Books, 1986. 224 pages.

Stafford, Tim. *The Sexual Christian.* Wheaton, Ill.: Victor Books, 1989. 197 pages.

Books about HIV and Drug Usage

Baucom, John. *Help Your Children Say No to Drugs.* Grand Rapids, Mich.: Zondervan Publishing House, 1987. 204 pages.

Campbell, Ross. *Your Child and Drugs: Help for Concerned Parents.* Wheaton.Ill.: Victor Books, 1988. 151 pages.

"Drugs, Sex, & AIDS." Free pamphlet published by the American Red Cross, 1730 D St. NW, Washington, D.C. 20006; 202/737–8300.

"Facts About AIDS & Drug Abuse." Free pamphlet published by the National AIDS Information Clearinghouse, P.O. Box 6003, Rockville, Md. 20850; 800/458–5231.

Perkins and Perkins. *Raising Drug-Free Kids in a Drug-Filled World,* New York: Harper & Row, 1989.

White, Betsy. *Smoke Screen.* Nashville: Abingdon Press, 1989. 288 pages.

NOTES

Chapter 2 AIDS: The Disease

1. J. Oleski et al., "Immune Deficiency in Children," *Journal of the American Medical Association* 249:2345–49.

2. Walter Batchelor, "The Science and the Limits of Science," *American Psychologist* 43, no. 11 (November 1988): 853.

3. Randy Shilts, *And the Band Played On* (New York: St. Martin's Press, 1987).

4. "Kaposi's sarcoma and Pneumocystis pneumonia among homosexual men—New York City and California," *Centers for Disease Control Morbidity and Mortality Weekly Reports* 30 (1981): 305–308.

5. "Human immunodeficiency virus infection in the United States: A review of current knowledge," *Centers for Disease Control Morbidity and Mortality Weekly Reports* 36 (1987): 137–40.

6. William Douglas, "Who Murdered Africa?" *Health Freedom News*, (September 1987): 8, 19, 40–42.

7. "AIDS: A guide for survival," *American Academy of Family Practice* (1988): 77.

8. J. R. Carlson, et al., "AIDS Serology Testing in Low- and High-Risk Groups," *Journal of the American Medical Association* 253 (1985): 3405–3408.

9. G. Werner, et al., "Prevalence of Serological Hepatitis A and A Markers in a Rural Area of Northern Zaire," *American Journal of Tropical Medicine and Hygiene* 34 (1985): 620–24.

10. William Masters, et al., *Crisis: Heterosexual Behavior in the Age of AIDS* (New York: Grove Press, 1988), 30–32.

11. *Surgeon General's Report on AIDS*, 1989.

12. "HIV-Related Knowledge and Behaviors Among High School Students," *Center for Disease Control, Morbidity and Mortality Weekly Reports* 39 (1990): 23.

13. Nicholas Hall, "The Virology of AIDS," *American Psychologist* 43, no. 11 (1988): 907–913.

14. Batchelor, 855–856.

15. Patrick Dixon, *The Whole Truth About AIDS* (Nashville: Thomas Nelson Publishers, 1989), 39–59.

16. *Surgeon General's Report on AIDS*, November 1989.

17. D. Des Jarlais and S. Friedman, "Target groups for preventing AIDS among intravenous drug users," *Journal of Applied Social Psychology* 17 (1987): 251–68.

18. Dixon, 81–83.

19. Hemophiliac Foundation statement quoted in Mason, et al., "AIDS, Hemophilia, and Prevention Efforts Within a Comprehensive Care Program," *American Psychologist*, 43, no. 11 (November 1988): 971–76.

20. Masters, pages 47–68.

21. Patricia Gadsby, "The Virus Strikes Back," *Discover* (July 1989): 20.

22. Shilts, *And the Band Played On*, 258.

23. June Reinisch, et al., "The study of sexual behavior in relation to the transmission of Human Immunodeficiency Virus," *American Psychologist* 43, no. 11 (1988): 921–27.

24. American College Health Association, in cooperation with the Centers for Disease Control: original data of fifteen cases of HIV positivity in the first five thousand samples tested. Study is to be published in a major journal in 1990.

25. David Van Biema, "What's Gone Wrong with Teen Sex?" *People* (17 April 1987): 111–21.

Chapter 3 AIDS: The Effects

1. J. Curran et al., "Acquired Immunodeficiency Syndrome associated with transfusions," *New England Journal of Medicine* 310 (1984): 69–75.

2. W. Bachelor, "AIDS 1988," *American Psychologist* 43, no. 11 (November 1988): 853–58.

3. "Information on AIDS for the Practicing Physician," American Medical Association publication, 1 (July 1987): 11.

4. "Information on AIDS for the Practicing Physician."

5. M. Krimm, "AIDS: The Challenge to Science and Medicine," *Quality Review Bulletin* 12, no. 8 (August 1986).

6. B. Navia, et al., "The AIDS Dementia Complex: Clinical Features," *Annals of Neurology* 19 (1986): 517–24.

7. Susan Tross and Dan Hirsch, "Psychological Distress and Neuropsychological Complications of HIV Infection and AIDS," *American Psychologist* 43, no. 11 (November 1988): 929–34.

8. New York State Health Department, Fall 1989.

9. U.S. Department of Health and Human Services Report, December 1988. Estimate of how many infants will be infected by 1991.

10. *Pediatric Annals* 17 (May 1988): 365; and *Pediatric Infectious Disease Journal* 7 (June 1988): 383.

11. "Coping with AIDS: Psychological and Social Considerations in Helping People with HTLV-III Infection," U.S. Department of Health and Human Services, 1987.

12. Robert Barret, "Counseling Gay Men with AIDS: Human Dimensions," *Journal of Counseling and Development* 67 (June 1989): 573–75.

13. Gregg Albers, *Counseling the Sick and Terminally Ill* (Waco, Tex.: Word, Inc., 1989), 18–20.

14. Albers, *Counseling the Sick and Terminally Ill.*

15. Hall, "The Virology of AIDS," 907–13.

16. Editorial, "HIV Counseling and Testing: Does it Work?" *American Journal of Public Health* 78, no. 12 (December 1988): 1533–34.

Chapter 4 AIDS: Addiction

1. Judd Marmor, ed., *Homosexual Behavior: A Modern Reappraisal* (New York: Basic Books, Inc., 1980), 10.

2. M. Duncan Stanton, Thomas C. Todd, et al., *The Family Therapy of Drug Abuse and Addiction* (New York: The Guilford Press, 1985), 22–30.

3. Letha Scanzoni and Virginia Mollenkott, *Is the Homosexual My Neighbor?* (New York: Harper and Row, Publishers, 1978), 95–96.

4. Bryan Magee, *One in Twenty: A Study of Homosexuality in Men and Women* (New York: Stein and Day, 1966), 29–33; Cynthia Lanning, ed., *Answers to Your Questions About Homosexuality* (Wilmore,

Ky.: Bristol Books, 1988), 109–12; and Clifford and Joyce Penner, *A Gift for All Ages* (Waco, Tex.: Word, Inc., 1986), 96–99.

5. Earl D. Wilson, *Counseling and Homosexuality* (Waco, Tex.: Word, Inc. 1988).

6. Michael Swift, *Gay Community News*, 15–21 February 1987.

7. Scanzoni and Mollenkott, 70–71.

8. 1972 Gay Rights Political Platform

9. *Journal of the American Medical Association* 263, no. 11 (16 March 1990): 1497.

10. Lanning, 103.

11. Wilson, 26.

12. Al Mooney and Carolyn Martin, *Alcohol and Drug Abuse,* American Academy of Family Physicians Home Study, Monograph 107, 1988.

13. Shilts, 24.

14. Penner, 253–65.

15. Patrick Carnes, *The Sexual Addiction* (Minneapolis: Comp Care Publications, 1983).

16. Medical school course work on human sexuality and nonjudgmental therapy.

17. Judith Reisman, Ph.D., The American University, unpublished study of pornography.

18. Susan Griffin, *Pornography and Silence* (New York: Harper and Row, Publishers, 1981), 103–104; and June Hopkins, ed., *Perspectives on Rape and Sexual Assault* (London: Harper and Row, Publishers, 1984), 30.

19. Sidney Cohen, M.D., *The Substance Abuse Problem* (New York: The Hayworth Press, 1981), 206–20.

20. Cohen, 213.

21. Martin Mawyer, *Silent Shame* (Westchester, Ill.: Crossway Books, 1987).

22. Ann Burgess, *Child Pornography and Sex Rings* (Lexington, Mass., D.C. Heath and Company, 1984), 86–101.

23. Josh McDowell, *What I Wish My Parents Knew About My Sexuality* (San Bernadino, Calif.: Here's Life Publishers, Inc., 1987).

24. Gregg Albers, *Plague in Our Midst* (Lafayette, La.: Huntington House, Inc.), 1988.

Chapter 5 AIDS: Ethics

1. Lorraine Day, "AIDS Risks to Health Care Personnel," San Francisco General Hospital Workshop publication, 1988; and

"Recommendations for Prevention of HIV Transmission in Health-Care Settings," *Centers for Disease Control Morbidity and Mortality Weekly Report*, 36, no. 2S (21 August 1987).

2. Gregory Herek and Eric Glunt, "An Epidemic of Stigma: Public Reactions to AIDS," *American Psychologist*, 43, no. 11 (November 1988): 886.

3. Gregg Albers, testimony before Subcommitee on Health and Environment, 21 September 1987.

4. Peterman, et al., *Journal of the American Medical Association* 29 (1 January 1988): 55.

5. Wolker Wahn, "Horizontal Transmission of HIV Infection between Two Siblings," *The Lancet* (20 September 1986), 694.

6. James Childress, *Priorities in Biomedical Ethics*, (Philadelphia: The Westminster Press, 1981), 1981.

7. J. Brown, *The High Cost of Healing* (New York: Human Sciences Press, Inc., 1985), 19–20.

8. Robert Buckingham, *The Complete Hospice Guide* (New York: Harper and Row, Publishers, 1983).

9. Tom Beauchamp and James Childress, *Principles of Biomedical Ethics* (New York: Oxford University Press, 1979), 75.

10. Day, "AIDS Risks to Health Care Personnel."

11. Dixon, 77.

Chapter 6 Counseling Those Who Need Testing

1. E. Rueda and M. Schwartz, *Gays, AIDS and You* (Old Greenwich, Conn.: The Devin Adair Company, 1987), 8.

2. D. Lyter, et al., "The HIV antibody test: Why gay and bisexual men want or do not want their results," *Public Health Reports* 102 (1987): 468–74.

3. T. J. Coates, et al., "AIDS Antibody Testing: Will it stop the AIDS Epidemic?" *American Psychologist* (43) no. 11 (November 1988): 859–64.

4. Coates, 859.

5. "AIDS: A Guide for Survival," *American Academy of Family Physicians* (April 1988), 27.

6. "Transmission of HIV," *American Family Physician* 37, no.4 (April 1988): 308–13.

7. Steven Miles, "Diagnosis and Staging of HIV Infection," *American Family Physician* 38, no. 4 (October 1988): 248–56.

8. Miles, 251.

9. *AIDS: Information on AIDS for the Practicing Physician* 1, American Medical Association (July 1987): 10.

10. Miles, 254.

11. Thomas Coates, "Consequences of AIDS antibody testing among gay and bisexual men," *Journal of the American Medical Association* 258, no. 1889 (June 1989).

12. W. Cates, and H. Handsfield, "HIV Counseling and Testing: Does it Work?" *American Journal of Public Health* 78, no. 12 (December 1988): 1533–34.

13. Gary R. Collins, *Innovative Approaches to Counseling* (Waco, Tex.: Word, Inc., 1986), 89–106.

14. Albers, *Counseling the Sick,* 75.

15. L. Peterson, "Adolescent Abstinence: A Guide for Family Planning Professionals," pamphlet produced by the Office of Population Affairs, 1988.

Chapter 7 Counseling When the Test Is Positive

1. J. Smith, et al., "Everyday Ethics in AIDS Care," *AIDS Patient Care* (October 1989), 27.

2. Everett L. Worthington, Jr., *Counseling for Unplanned Pregnancy and Infertility,* (Waco, Tex.: Word, Inc., 1987), 71–109.

3. "AIDS: A Guide for Survival," American Academy of Family Physicians publication (1988): 38–39.

4. Herbert Benson et al., *Managing Stress* (Alexandria, Va.: Time-Life Books, 1987), 11–13.

5. Albers, *Counseling the Sick,* 3–32.

6. R. Kalish, *Death, Grief, and Caring Relationships,* (Brooks/ Cole Publishing Co., 1985).

7. Albers, *Counseling the Sick,* 113–17.

8. S. Wilson, "AIDS Dementia Complex," *AIDS Patient Care* (1989): 20.

9. *AIDS: Information on AIDS for the Practicing Physician,* 1, American Medical Association (July 1987): 11.

10. Dixon, 72–73.

11. No one will admit that casual contact can even rarely spread AIDS. But many medical experts are encouraging people who have cuts and may be exposed to an HIV-positive person, to cover those cuts with an antibiotic ointment and a bandage to ensure that the virus and any bacteria do not infect the cut.

12. J. Calabrese, et al., "Alterations in Immunocompetence During Stress, Bereavement, and Depression," *American Journal of Psychiatry* 144 (1987): 1123.

13. Senate Subcommittee Testimony

14. G. Friedland and R. Lkein, "Transmission of the Human Immunodeficiency Virus," *New England Journal of Medicine,* 317 (29 October, 1987): 1125–35.

Chapter 8 Counseling Those Who Are Ill

1. Savine Weizman and Phyllis Kamm, *About Mourning: Support and Guidance for the Bereaved,* (New York: Human Sciences Press), 1985.

2. Albers, *Counseling the Sick,* 11–50.

3. Benson, *Managing Stress.*

4. Albers,*Counseling the Sick,* 15–18.

5. J. Brooks-Gunn, et al., "Preventing HIV Infection and AIDS in Children," *American Psychologist* 43, no. 11 (November 1988): 958–64.

6. Robert Long, *Drugs and American Society* (New York: H. W. Wilson, 1986), 115–16.

7. Albers, *Counseling the Sick,* 22–26.

8. E. Kübler-Ross, *On Death and Dying* (New York: Macmillan, 1969).

9. Albers, *Counseling the Sick,* 26–32, 85–90.

10. R. C. Sproul, *Surprised by Suffering* (Wheaton, Ill.: Tyndale House, 1989), 73–88.

11. A. Baum and S. Nesselhof, "Psychological Research and the Prevention, Etiology, and Treatment of AIDS," *American Psychologist* 43, no. 11 (November 1988): 900–906.

12. J. Kiecold-Glaser and R. Glaser, "Psychosocial moderators of immune function," *Annals of Behavioral Medicine* 9, no. 2 (1986): 5–21.

13. Albers, *Counseling the Sick,* 30–32.

14. Paul Johnson and Larry Richards, *Spiritual Secrets to Physical Health,* (Waco, Tex.: Word, Inc., 1987), 45–58, 78–97.

15. M. Gold, *The Good News about Depression,* (New York: Villard Books, 1987), 104–15.

16. K. Taylor, "Neuropsychiatric Management of AIDS," *AIDS Patient Care* (June 1987): 8.

17. Gold, 167–181.

Chapter 9 Counseling the Terminally Ill

1. E. Kübler-Ross, *On Death and Dying*.
2. L. Bugen, *Death and Dying: Theory/Research/Practice* (Dubuque, Iowa: Brown, 1979).
3. Miles, 248–56.
4. N. Pelosi, "AIDS and Public Policy," *American Psychologist* 43, no. 11 (November 1988): 844.
5. B. Spring and E. Larson, *Euthanasia: Spiritual, Medical, and Legal Issues in Terminal Health Care* (Portland, Ore.: Multnomah, 1988), 31.
6. M. Albers, "A Buddy's Story," an unpublished personal account of involvement in an AIDS buddy program, 1989.
7. K. Schemmer, et al., *Between Life and Death: The Life Support Dilemma*, (Wheaton, Ill.: Victor Books, 1988), 28–35.
8. Informal survey of health professionals suggests a change in attitude over the past ten years toward utilization of "heroic measures" of prolonging life. A broad majority stated preference for patient control, home environment, and psychological support instead of physical life prolongation.
9. Schemmer, *Between Life and Death*, 86.

Chapter 10 Counseling the Family of AIDS Patients

1. Brooks-Gunn, "Preventing HIV Infection," 958–64.
2. Informal studies in 1985 showed that only 20 percent of parents were discussing and teaching their children about sexuality. The same study repeated in 1990 showed that 40 percent of parents are now discussing sexuality with their children. AIDS has been the primary motivation for this change.
3. Albers, *Counseling the Sick*, 145–47.
4. Emotional stimulation within the brain has direct communicating tracts to the autonomic nervous system which regulates adrenalin, heart rate, breathing rate, skin sweating, and a number of other functions which give a person the "feelings" of fright, joy, anger, and elation.
5. J. LaMontague and M. Meyer, "Clinical Trials of Drugs for the Treatment of AIDS: Information for the Practicing Physician," *American Medical Association*, 3 (1987).
6. R. Eyer, "Caring for Homosexuals with AIDS," *Leadership Magazine* (Spring 1988), 100–102.

7. Eyer, "Caring for Homosexuals," 101.

8. Al Mooney and Carolyn Martin, *Alcohol and Drug Abuse,* American Academy of Family Physicians Home Study Program, Monograph 107 (1988): 31–33.

9. Patsy Crandall, "Codependency," *The Virginia Baptist Hospital Mental Health and Substance Abuse Newsdigest,* April 1990.

10. P. El-Mallakh and R. El-Mallakh, "Group Psychotherapy for AIDS Patients," *AIDS Patient Care* (December 1989): 18–20.

11. Albers, *Counseling the Sick,* 69–90.

12. I have been unable to find any studies of the grief or dying process in AIDS patients. A need exists to study this area to delineate the complicating emotional components in more detail.

13. Eyer, "Caring for Homosexuals," 101.

14. J. Phillips, "AIDS and ARC: Pastoral Issues in the Hospital Setting," *Journal of Religion and Health* 27, no. 2 (Summer 1988): 119–28.

15. P. Mason, et al., "AIDS, Hemophilia, and Prevention Efforts Within a Comprehensive Care Program," *American Psychologist* 43, no. 11 (November 1988): 971–76.

Chapter 11 The Church's Role in AIDS

1. This number has been given as the total number of HIV positive persons by the Centers for Disease Control, the National Institutes of Health since 1987. It is highly likely we have more than three million persons infected since we have over one million persons with ARC and AIDS.

2. W. Masters, V. Johnson, and R. Kolodony, *Crisis: Heterosexual Behavior in the Age of AIDS* (New York: Grove Press, 1988), 4.

3. The figure (10 million) infected with HIV is an estimate based on information from the Public Health Service, present trends of the epidemic, and simple exponential growth that has occurred to date. Most experts are reluctant to form estimates because of the many variables involved with the future course of the epidemic.

4. McDowell, "What I Wish My Parents Knew."

5. D. Barnes, "Drugs: Running the Numbers," *Science* 240 (24 June 1988), 1729–31.

6. Albers, *Plague in Our Midst,* 161–72.

7. Psalm 106; Numbers 25.

8. "MAP International, The Church's Response to the Challenge of AIDS/HIV," Copyright 1990 by Americans for a Sound AIDS/HIV Policy and MAP International.

9. Baptist Church, Charlottesville, Virginia
10. Josh McDowell Ministries, P.O. Box 1000, Dallas, Texas 75221.
11. Previously mentioned informal survey that showed only 20 percent of parents educating their chidren about sexuality in 1985, which has increased to 40 percent by 1990.
12. M. Albers, "A Buddy's Story."
13. Dixon, "The Whole Truth," 151–53.
14. Dixon, "The Whole Truth," 152.
15. Exodus International, P.O. Box 2121, San Raphael, CA 94912.
16. El-Mallakh and El-Mallakh, "Group Psychotherapy," 18–20.

INDEX

Faith, 18
Family, 56
Fear, 77, 112, 120, 179, 188
Fever, 132
"Fight or flight," 120
First aid, 128
Foreign travel, 20
Free clinic, 199
Funeral, 160
Fungal infection, 43

"Gay," 20
Gay Bowel Syndrome, 40
Gay-related Immunodeficiency (GRID), 34
Gay Rights Movement, 65
Gonorrhea, 40, 93
Goals, 145, 148
Grief, 52, 57, 121, 138, 154, 169, 172, 178
Grief, pathologic, 121–22, 135, 143, 179; grief, personality, 139
Gross national product, 80
Growth, 58, 120, 143–44
Guilt, 54, 56, 121, 180
Gunshot, 14

Haiti, 10–11, 106
Hallucinogens, 69
Harassment, 76
Healing, 160
Health care, 80
Health department, 190
Heart attack, 12, 57
Helplessness, 138
Hemophilia/hemophiliac, 5–6, 30, 49, 151, 174, 180
Heroin, 12, 14, 16, 69, 115
Herpes, 4–5, 20, 33, 48, 95, 97

Heterosexual, 8, 13, 20–21, 35, 37, 51, 56, 67,
Homosexuality, 8, 14, 21, 30, 34, 37, 51, 56, 61, 66, 85, 98, 108, 140, 154, 169, 172, 181
Honesty, 93, 123
Hospice, 156, 180, 194
Housing, 79, 127
Human bites, 78
Human sacrifice, 15
Human T-Lymphocyte Virus III (HTLV III), 28
Hypersexuality, 67
Hyperventilation, 52
Hysteria, 138–39, 170

Immune system, 25, 43, 124, 148
Impotence, 146
Incest, 59, 173
Infections, 13, 85
Infidelity, 57
Influenza, 29
Injections, 11, 42, 62
Insect, 75
Insight, 143
Insurance, 79
Intercourse, 30, 36, 45, 68, 72
Interferon, 119
Intimate contact, 77
Intoxication, 69
Intravenous (IV), 16, 30, 53, 68; IV drug users, 21, 25, 106, 169

Judgment, 35, 46, 53, 59, 69, 169

Kaposi's sarcoma, 34, 133
Kissing, 78
Kübler-Ross, Elisabeth, 154

Gregg R. Albers, M.D., F.A.A.F.P.

Gregg R. Albers is a practicing family physician in Lynchburg, Virginia. He serves as director of Health Services at Liberty University and teaches at Liberty University. Dr. Albers is a member of the Christian Medical Society and the American Academy of Family Practice. In addition to a number of articles in specialty and Christian magazines, he has authored *Plague in Our Midst: Sexuality, AIDS, and the Christian Family* and *Counseling the Sick and Terminally Ill.*

Dr. Albers received his B.A. from Miami University, his M.D. from the Medical College of Ohio, and his Family Practice residency from Mercy Hospital, Toledo, Ohio. He and his wife Andrea are members of Thomas Road Baptist Church in Lynchburg, Virginia; they have two daughters, Bethany and Rachel, and two sons, Wesley and Andrew.